# THE GREAT GUN-MAKER

*The Story of Lord Armstrong*

by

## DAVID DOUGAN

**SANDHILL
PRESS**

First published by Frank Graham in 1970.

© David Dougan

This reprint published in 1991
by Sandhill Press Ltd., 17, Castle Street,
Warkworth, Morpeth,
Northumberland,
NE65 0UW.

ISBN 0946098 23 9

Cover Illustration: *Light  Gun Fitting Shop*
Courtesy of Vickers PLC Defence Systems.

The Publishers gratefully acknowledge the assistance of Newcastle upon
Tyne City Libraries & Arts, Tyne & Wear Archives, Vickers PLC
Defence Systems in providing photographs for this reprint.

Printed by St. Edmundsbury Press.

*For Eileen*

# Contents

# Illustrations

# *Preface*

IN writing this short biography of Lord Armstrong, I have become indebted to a number of people. Six of them I should mention in particular.

David Reed, the young, energetic press officer for Vickers on Tyneside and now a Member of Parliament, accepted the idea of such a book wholeheartedly as soon as I put it to him. He not only secured the co-operation of his company and of many of the present staff who proved invaluable to me, but also smoothed my path in various other ways. The present Lord and Lady Armstrong showed great kindness and hospitality and gave me quite a lot of useful information about the personal life of the first Lord and Lady Armstrong. Miss June Thompson, the local history specialist at Newcastle City Library, was as usual continuously helpful and charming, and Mr Jim Allison of Vickers read the draft manuscript. Finally, I must thank most warmly my wife Eileen, who not only helped me with much of the research but also undertook the considerable task of typing the manuscript.

For all errors and for all expressions of opinion, I alone am responsible. I can but hope that those who helped me so much will not think their efforts have been in vain.

DAVID DOUGAN,
*Newcastle,* 1970.

# Introduction

I F you search among the shelves of biographical works in most public libraries looking for the lives of the great engineers, you will no doubt find the stories of George and Robert Stephenson, of James Watt, of the Brunels, Charles Parsons, Joseph Whitworth, Trevithick and many others. But you will probably be surprised by numerous anomalies and deficiencies. One of the most obvious is the life story of William George Armstrong, first Baron of Cragside.

At least to people living in the north and more particularly on Tyneside, the deficiency might seem surprising. Elsewhere, Armstrong's name may now have no meaning. Yet a hundred years ago, he was a man not only of national but of international stature. For he shared with Alfred Krupp of Germany the reputation of being the greatest manufacturer of armaments in the world. Where the Krupp family lived on for another four generations personifying the production of weapons of death right up to our own time, Armstrong had no heirs. His firm was left to others and now is part of the Vickers Group of Companies. The works which he formed on Tyneside are still in existence, still turning out armaments or engineering goods. But, although it is vaguely remembered locally, his name has long since vanished from national consciousness.

Yet as both an inventor and a manufacturer, Armstrong was as important as, say, the Stephensons, the Brunels or any other engineer of that century. And his contribution to the armaments industry—with all the complicated moral issues that that raised—was such that it seems incredible his name is now forgotten. During the second half of the nineteenth century, when he was personally in charge of one of the largest and most powerful arsenals in the world, thousands of cannons and millions of shells were produced on Tyneside for sale not only to the British Government but to many foreign countries too. It was an industrial success story of enormous proportions. It was also something more : one of the most frightening hostages to fortune one could imagine.

In the final quarter of the century, his interest swung from land-based armaments to naval warfare. He became a great supplier first of naval weapons and then of whole warships. The output was for sale to anyone or any country. Of course, sales were not made intentionally to enemies of this country but the difficulty was one never knew who one's enemies might be. Certainly, there were no scruples even of this kind in selling to two foreign countries who might find themselves at war. In fact, there were numerous examples of opposing countries buying their armaments from him.

It is tempting of course to condemn Armstrong, to follow the line taken by one of the newspaper obituaries: 'There is something that appals the imagination in the application of a cool and temperate mind like Lord Armstrong's to the science of destruction.' But is it entirely fair? Armstrong himself thought that by improving the quality of weapons, by increasing their range, he was helping to reduce the brutality of war. Anything that prevented men from fighting hand to hand in close combat must be an advance, he argued. He also took a stand that is now familiar : that the scientist and the engineer supplied the means but it was society that decided on the ends. Certainly he was given overwhelming support for such a view not only in the public admiration he received but in tangible rewards, such as honours or profits. He was seen to be a great national benefactor, a man who had played a signal part in increasing the security of this country and the defence of the Empire. That this view should not have altered radically when he started to sell arms to other countries too is one of the major mysteries of this story.

Whatever may be one's feelings on the moral dilemma, there seems little doubt that the work of people like Armstrong played a significant part in promoting the arms race that has been going on ever since. Granted that the emergence of nations and of national armies, as distinct from relatively small, private ones, provided the stimulus to demand, nevertheless the technical improvements not only to the weapons themselves but to their manufacture made it far easier for that demand to be met.

There was, however, one telling and perhaps in the end irrefutable argument. Since there was a clearly expressed demand for weapons, a supply would be forthcoming. It was far better that that supply should spring from one's own country than from another. In that way, other countries would both be dependent upon this one and behind this one. For the latest fruits of research would be available to the home government first. It was in this light that Armstrong's work was recognised. As an admirer declared: 'I say we may confidently anticipate that while we have among us men like Sir William Armstrong, this country will be found behind no other in the efficiency of its armaments.'

While armaments and the moral dilemma they pose provide the main fascination of Armstrong's life, there is much else too. He made many path-breaking contributions to the sciences of hydraulics and electricity. He carried out important investigations into the wasteful use of coal. He conducted valuable experiments into the relative strength of metals.

He was even much more than an important scientific figure. He was also a major manufacturer, turning a small factory employing a handful of men into a giant concern employing 20,000 by the time he died. A contemporary account written just before his death recorded: 'Extended and complete as they are today, there is not another institution like the Elswick Works in the United Kingdom—probably not another in the world ... Their size, their completeness, their tremendous productive energy, their variety of blast furnaces, foundries, machine shops and chemical laboratories, teeming with human life, reverberating with the shriek of steam, the clang of hammers and the whirr of machinery, overhung by a pillar of cloud by day and of fire by night, present a picture of concentrated industrial activity which overwhelms and astonishes the average observer!'

Take away the element of hyperbole and the story is still exciting and impressive, especially since Armstrong did not start his factory until he was thirty-seven years of age.

# CHAPTER ONE

## NEWCASTLE: AN ENGINEERING CENTRE

NEWCASTLE in the early nineteenth century: a good place and time to be born an engineer. Fifty miles away or a hundred years earlier and 'industry' might have been an idea that was scarcely understood and a word that was rarely used. But an inquisitive boy growing up in the Newcastle of the second and third decades of the nineteenth century could hardly fail to appreciate the exciting developments that were taking place in what was still basically a mediaeval town. He would see them on his way to school, read of them in the daily or weekly journals, hear his parents or their friends talk of them. In that sense the birth of William George Armstrong in Newcastle on 26th November 1810 could not have been more aptly arranged.

Of course some industry, particularly mining, was centuries old. 'Coals from Newcastle' was already a national and indeed an international phrase. Great fleets of colliers sailed from the Tyne, not only to London but also to France, Germany and the Low Countries. Originally, because of the transport problem, coal-mining was confined to the immediate vicinity of the rivers. But the development of wooden wagon ways eased the transport difficulty and allowed the exploitation of reserves further away. As early as 1630, for example, mining was going on at Chopwell and Blackburn, four to five miles up the Derwent Valley in County Durham. By 1700 Tanfield Moor and Pontop, ten miles up the valley, were being exploited.

Coal was not the only industrial attraction. By the late seventeenth century a number of iron and lead works had sprung up. There was a blast furnace and forge at Allensford Mill. There was another iron forge at Derwentcote. A steel works was established at Blackhill Mill. The Hollow Sword-Blade Company built works at Shotley Bridge and the London

Lead Company bought smelt-mills at Ryton early in the
eighteenth century. A paper works was set up at Chopwell at
about the same time.

Above all, Ambrose Crowley built an iron works at Win-
laton in 1697 and this turned the valley into an industrial
centre. The development of coal and other trades stimulated
shipbuilding. The ships were mostly colliers, the quality of
the work was not high and all the scores of businesses that
sprang up eventually collapsed. The iron works too began to
fail so that by the end of the eighteenth century the Derwent
Valley was a declining area. Many of the national developments in iron and steel making passed it by. Even the Crowley
works faded away and were eventually given over to light
engineering.

All these activities were little more than pinpricks in a
fabric that was still essentially mediaeval. Even by the end of
the eighteenth century, Newcastle city wall with its seven
gates was still intact. There was only one bridge across the
river. The castle was the county gaol. Streets were unlit at
night. Sanitation was primitive.

Yet slowly life was changing. More people were living outside the city walls in suburbs to the west and north. There
was a noticeable increase in the number of charity schools,
founded by the wealthier inhabitants. The boys were taught
reading and writing; the girls more practical household accom-
plishments such as knitting and sewing. A general infirmary
was opened at Forth Banks in 1752. There were 90 beds and
two surgeons. A few years later, a lying-in hospital—or
maternity home—for poor women was opened.

These signs of progress contrasted with the continuing
traditions. Blood sports, such as cock-fighting or bull-baiting,
were still very popular among all classes. There were successful
cockpits at the Bull and Crown in the Flesh Market and at
the Turks Head Hotel in Bigg Market. Betting was frequently
heavy. The pillory and the public gallows were still used and
transportation was another alternative.

But slowly the growth of industries—coal, iron, shipbuilding—the spread of trade and the introduction of mechanical
methods began to change not only the types of work but also
the pattern of life. Newcastle was slowly emerging from a

backwater into a new world. In fact, with four other towns—
Manchester, Birmingham, Leeds and Glasgow—it could be
said to have been leading the way for the rest of the country
into the new world.

The Tyne was one of the first rivers in the country to offer
a steamboat service. In May 1814, only two years after Henry
Bell's Comet pioneered the first steam service on a British
river, the 'Tyne Steam Packet' began to convey passengers
between South Shields and Newcastle. In 1820, when young
Armstrong was ten years old, Robert and William Hawthorn
formed a partnership to run an engine works at Forth Banks,
Newcastle, and in their first year they built three pairs of
engines for steam packets running on the Tyne.

Their father, also called Robert, was considered the most
famous enginewright on Tyneside at the turn of the century.
In 1790, when he was only twenty years old, he had been
made chief engineer at Walbottle Colliery in Northumberland.
A neighbour in the row of single storey cottages were he lived
was Robert Stephenson, whose son George was to become
the famous locomotive engineer. In fact he began to make his
reputation in the early 1820's, when William Armstrong was
still a lad, by building the Stockton and Darlington Railway
which in 1825 became the first public railway in the world
to carry passengers.

The Hawthorn brothers were quickly followed by Hawks,
Crawshay and Company at Gateshead and then by George
Stephenson who set up a company to build railway equipment
and locomotives in 1823. The stimulus that the steam engine
and the locomotive gave to Tyneside engineering raised the
district to national importance. For years, Newcastle engineers,
led by the Hawthorns and by Stephenson, remained the sole
producers of locomotive engines in the world. Fifteen miles
south, the river Wear was establishing a reputation for shipbuilding. The North Sands was thronged with yards in the
1820's and 1830's.

It was into this new world of innovation that William
Armstrong was so appropriately born in 1810, eight years
after his sister, Anne.

## WILLIAM ARMSTRONG, SENIOR

Their father, also called William, was a corn-merchant. He had left home at Wreay, five miles south of Carlisle, where his father John was a shoemaker, to come to Newcastle. William, who was born in 1778, was only a youth at the time but he was invited to become a clerk to Losh, Lubben and Company, corn-merchants in Cowgate. A few years later, the elderly partners retired and Armstrong became the sole owner. He changed the name to Armstrong and Company.

The retirement of the partners was a singular piece of good fortune but Armstrong himself was an extraordinary man. To be able to read and write at that time, seventy years before compulsory education, was an accomplishment of the minority. His academic interest went much further than that, however. He was fascinated by mathematics and he contributed numerous articles on the subject to various magazines. He also acquired a substantial library of mathematical books and when he died almost 1,300 of them were given to the Literary and Philosophical Society in Newcastle, a body he had joined in 1799, at the age of 21, six years after its founding.

Late in life, in fact when he was approaching 60, he became interested in public affairs. Perhaps the stimulus was provided by the Municipal Corporations Act of 1835. Until that time, few householders had any share in their own government. The local councils were small, self-perpetuating and corrupt. In virtually every town a considerable part of the income derived from market tolls, river dues and the like, went straight into the pockets of the councillors. The 1835 Act eradicated some of the deficiencies. The most important change was the widening of the franchise to include all rate-paying householders. The Act also widened the boundaries of certain towns. Newcastle was now to include the formerly separate villages of Westgate, Elswick, Jesmond, Heaton and Byker.

It was for the new Jesmond ward that William Armstrong stood as a candidate. His opponent was Matthew Anderson, and the main issue between them was the future of the Mansion House. Anderson argued in favour of maintaining the centuries-long tradition of the Mayor living luxuriously

at the ratepayers' expense. Armstrong wanted reform, partial
if not total. So did most of the electors and they gave him
an easy victory on 1st November 1836.

In January 1836 the council decided by a majority of 25 to
21 that the Mansion House system should be reformed. In
future the Mayor would receive £1,000 a year to keep up
'certain restricted hospitalities', and he should normally live
in his own house.

When Armstrong came up for re-election, he was defeated
by 38 votes to 8. It was a sad blow, one of the few in a long
life usually marked by success. But three years later his
opponent retired and Armstrong was able to resume his seat
unopposed.

He was getting on by this time. But even though he was
65 he clearly enjoyed council work and became especially
interested in the development of the river Tyne. He wrote a
couple of pamphlets on the subject and was made chairman
of the River Committee. In this position he was involved in
many of the investigations and discussions which eventually
led to the creation of the River Tyne Commission. It was
probably his work in this connection that ensured his unani-
mous election as alderman in 1849. A few months later he
was even nominated for Mayor. His proposer, Alderman
Joseph Lamb, said of him : 'He has been a zealous, active and
industrious merchant for the last fifty years.' He had been
'ten times a deputy to London and other places for the benefit
of the town'. Even so, the majority felt that his opponent,
Mr Joseph Crawhall was the better candidate. But the following year at the age of 74, Armstrong was successful in
becoming Mayor.

He seems to have been a worthy, if dull, incumbent. But a
contemporary account of his generous hospitality when he
gave a grand ball in the Assembly Rooms, stated that 'the
attention of the Mayor and Mrs W. G. Armstrong (his
daughter-in-law) to their guests was most unremitting throughout the evening, and refreshments were served out with great
profusion and liberality ... The arrangements for the occasion
were conducted in the usual style of magnificence and hospitality and the whole affair passed off to the unmixed enjoyment and satisfaction of the brilliant gathering'.

On his retirement from that office, Alderman Joseph Lamb proposed a vote of thanks. He said that Armstrong, 'by his kindness of manners on the bench and his impartiality and affability in the chair had given universal satisfaction to the council and won golden opinions from the public'.

As a politician, Armstrong was a mild reformer. He wanted to moderate the scale of luxury afforded to the Mayor and he helped to replace the separate river authorities by the Tyne Commissioners who would be responsible for the improvement of the whole river. But he could not always be relied upon by the progressives. He opposed the building of a railway between Newcastle and Carlisle. He thought a canal was the better proposition and said so forcefully at a public meeting in the Moot Hall, Newcastle, in 1824. Twenty years later when the Town Council was considering asking Parliament to abolish the Corn Laws, thus allowing the free import of grain, he argued in favour of their retention.

Socially, he seems to have been well-liked. Certainly he had a wide circle of friends. One of the most important was Armorer Donkin, a solicitor, who played an influential part in the development of young William's career. Donkin was the son of a South Shields' timber merchant. He was articled to a solicitor in the town, completed his training in London, then returned to Newcastle in 1801 just after both his parents had died. Armorer Donkin set up in business on his own account. At first, his practice was slow to develop. He thus found plenty of time to indulge his hobbies of reading and performing scientific experiments. It was a natural thing for him to join the Literary and Philosophical Society. There he met William Armstrong senior and they became intimate friends. Donkin seems to have been slightly more successful than Armstrong in business, or perhaps he had fewer commitments for he remained a bachelor all his life. Anyway, he was able to acquire an imposing house, now demolished, in Jesmond Park. There he often entertained. Every Sunday morning he put on a lunch for his friends. He called it 'Donkin's ordinary' but the guests were hardly ordinary. They sometimes contained figures like Ramsay, the portrait painter, or Leigh Hunt, the essayist. His obituary said of him : 'For thirty years he stood at the head of his profession, conducting a large and varied practice; and his clients were not confined to this town and neighbourhood alone but many of the principal families in the neighbouring counties confided their properties and their interests to his skill and protection. If there was one trait which distinguished him more than another it was the extreme cordiality and sincerity of his attachments to his friends ... In personal appearance he was stout and in his later years somewhat corpulent. His head and face, though not handsome, were cast in a noble and massive mould; and a look of peculiar intelligence, mingled with good humour, and a great self-possession, generally lighted up his countenance. A hearty joyousness, and a desire to communicate the pleasure he felt, were the prevailing features of his address.'

More important, from our point of view, he took a great liking to the two children of his friend William Armstrong. They visited him frequently, treating him like a second father, and often spent school holidays at Donkin's country house at Rothbury. He eventually took William junior into his business and when he died he left young Armstrong his considerable fortune. But we are moving ahead too quickly.

## ARMSTRONG, THE BOY

William was born at No. 9 Pleasant Row, one of a terrace of plain-fronted, three-storeyed houses, each with a frontage of 24 feet. There was no garden in front but a small one at the rear leading down to Pandon Dene. The site is now part of a virtually derelict railway goods yard in Falconer Street.

Young William suffered from poor health as a boy. The northern climate did not help and for months on end, through winter and early spring, he was confined to the home, fending for himself for amusement. He seems to have found that no difficulty. He would make his own toy machines from old spinning wheels or other suitable objects. He often used weights, tied to pieces of string dropped over the stair bannisters, to give them power and movement. Occasionally his father's friends brought him toys but it was not so much the presents themselves as the way they worked that fascinated him. When the warmer days came and he could go out, he would spend much of his time in the shop of a joiner, John Fordy, where he was allowed to make fittings for his model machines. Here he learnt the use of tools, a practical interest that never left him throughout his life.

For his education, he was sent to a number of private schools in Newcastle, then to a school in Whickham, Northumberland, and finally in 1826, at the age of 16, to a grammar school in Bishop Auckland. He stayed there two years, boarding with the master, the Rev. R. Thompson, in his house on the south side of the market place.

On the opposite side of the street lived an old woman. One day she discovered that all her windows had been cracked. A look-out was kept and it was found that young Armstrong was the culprit. He had made himself a crossbow and using broken stems of tobacco pipes as missiles, he fired them from his bedroom at the old woman's windows. He was punished and had to pay for the damage. But that he attempted the trick in the first place and then that he did not own up shows that after all he was a normal mischievous lad rather than the somewhat prissy young genius he is so often depicted.

Bishop Auckland, although a rural backwater, did possess at that time an engineering works, owned by William Ramshaw. As one would expect, Armstrong developed the habit of calling there and eventually he was invited to the proprietor's house. There he met the proprietor's daughter, Margaret Ramshaw, who was later to become his wife.

As his school days drew to a close, Armstrong started to think more and more seriously about what he should do in life. Mechanics was the subject that fascinated him. It always had from his earliest days. Now he was more addicted than ever. But at that time it was hardly a proper calling. True, there were remarkable developments in the machinery used at collieries. And one or two people were beginning to talk of railways as a means of transporting goods and perhaps even people. But it was all so nebulous, so indefinite. And the sort of people in this business. They were rough, lacking charm. Armstrong senior had left that uncouth world. He did not want his son to plunge back into it. He wanted him to have a real profession, to exploit his education in a way that he, the father, had not been able to do. What better chance could there be than to become articled to his crony Armorer Donkin? And so it was done. Young Armstrong protested but not very loudly. He had no definite alternative plans to put forward. And, after all, Donkin was a great friend, a second father. It would do.

## ARMSTRONG, THE YOUNG MAN

It was around this time that Donkin arranged for his friend Ramsay to paint young Armstrong's portrait. A flattering job he made of it. Certainly Armstrong was a good-looking young man. But here he is invested with a romantic, wistful, appealing quality. The eyes are soft and gentle; the lips full with a hint of a Cupid's bow; the hair dark and curly. Only the nose has a sharpness about it, expressive of the powerful sense of purpose that the other features might belie. Even so the overall impression is one of a gentle dreamer or perhaps of a young man of means. This is not an embryo engineer who does not mind getting his hands dirty and who loves nothing better than handling tools.

Perhaps it was part of a clever plot to convince young William that the law was really much nicer. For three or four years he stayed in Donkin's chambers. Then he went down to London to be coached by his late sister's husband, W. H. Watson, a special pleader at the Temple.

Anne had married William Harry Watson in 1826 when she was 24 years of age. Two years later she was dead, a few months after the birth of her only child, John William. Watson married again in 1831.

In 1833 Armstrong returned to Newcastle and in 1835, at the age of 25, he was admitted into partnership with his friend Armorer Donkin and his colleague, G. W. Stable. The business was known as Donkin, Stable and Armstrong. The following year he married his boyhood sweetheart Margaret Ramshaw. He was not unhappy with the prospects by any means but now it looked as if the dye, which his father had wanted, was well and truly cast.

But perhaps not quite. Armorer Donkin continues to play a fundamentally influential part in Armstrong's career, a much more important part than his father. For Donkin was

sympathetic whereas his own father was critical of the young
man's engineering ambitions. Alfred Cochrane, son-in-law of
Armstrong's great confederate-to-be, Andrew Noble, put it
this way: 'Lord Armstrong took many prudent steps but the
most prudent one was that of joining Mr Donkin in his office.
Every possible liberty seems to have been allowed him to
follow his own scientific researches ... At the same time, he
was really most fortunately situated, for while very little
restriction seems to have been placed upon his other interests,
he was able to put by a certain amount of money, which
afterwards came in very useful and his work not only kept
him directly in close touch with Mr Donkin but also indirectly brought him into connection with certain other
acquaintances who lent him most valuable support.'

Alfred Cochrane, writing in 1909, also coments upon Armstrong's work as a solicitor. 'I have seen it stated that Lord
Armstrong was not a success as a solicitor but I find no evidence to that effect. He was always a clear thinker and he had
a gift of lucid expression. I have read letters written by him,
when he was in Mr Donkin's firm, on legal matters, and you
find him handling complicated questions with great thoroughness.' But Cochrane does admit: 'As to the exact extent of his
legal attainments history is silent. He would certainly have
given shrewd advice to any enquiring client, though it is
conceivable that such advice might have been based less upon
a profound knowledge of the law, than on sound common-
sense.'

But clearly the law was not his first love or interest. Armstrong himself said: 'The law was not, of course, of my own
choosing; my vocation was chosen for me and for a good
many years I stuck to the law while all my leisure was given
to mechanics. But the circumstances were peculiar. A great
friend of my family's, Mr Donkin, had a very prosperous
attorney's business. He was childless. When I entered his
office, I was practically adopted by him; I was to be his heir.
Such an opening in life was, of course, most attractive; here
it seemed, was a career ready made for me. As it turned out,
of course, it meant the waste of some ten or eleven of the best
years of my life—and yet not entire waste, perhaps, for my
legal training and knowledge have been of help to me in many

ways in business. And all the time, although I had no idea of abandoning the law and regularly attended to my professional duties, I was an amateur scientist, constantly experimenting and studying in my leisure time.'[1]

In fact, one could say that during his eleven years as a solicitor he was serving his apprenticeship as an engineer for he spent his considerable free time in developing his mechanical knowledge and skill. He made almost daily visits to the High Bridge works of Mr Henry Watson and he took a great interest in the manufactures carried on there: the turret clocks, the theodolites, the telescopes. He became firm friends not only with Mr Watson but also with his assistant, Mr John Hutchinson, and with the two younger Hutchinsons who also worked in the business. It was at these works that his first machine was made in 1838. This was, essentially, a wheel which would apply the power of water to the driving of machinery. The idea came to Armstrong through his favourite hobby, fishing.

## THE BUDDING ENGINEER

While he was fishing for trout in the Yorkshire valley of Dentdale, he noticed the water wheel in operation at a marble works on the other bank. He noticed, too, that the wheel was functioning well below its potential because the flow of water was less than required. If a more regular flow of water could be achieved, by means of a pump, then much higher efficiency would result.

Armstrong himself put it this way: 'I was lounging idly about, watching an old water mill when it occurred to me what a small part of the power of the water was used in driving the wheel and then I thought how great would be the force of even a small quantity of water if its energy were only concentrated in one column.'[2]

He talked his idea over with Mr Watson and eventually produced his design for a rotatory hydraulic engine. Armstrong wrote an article on 'The Application of Water as a Motive Power for driving machinery'. This paper helped to establish his name as an amateur engineer of promise. But little real interest was shown in his idea. He decided, therefore, to have a working model made. By the end of 1839 it was ready. Using the pressure from the town's water pipes, the machine produced five horsepower. Again Armstrong pursued the subject in scientific magazines with the intention of calling attention to it. But again no one showed any real interest.

He decided to adapt the principle of water power to other uses. He abandoned the rotatory principle and introduced the single stroke of a piston. These modifications he applied to the design of a crane. But again his work elicited no positive interest, even though he went so far as to produce another working model which he tested with the town's water pipes.

Five years later a development occurred that provided an opening for his invention. For the moment, however, he was baulked. But just at that time something else caught William Armstrong's attention. He heard of a curious experience at Cramlington Colliery in Northumberland. William Patterson was operating a fixed high pressure steam engine there when he happened to lay a hand on the safety valve just at the moment when the other hand was in contact with steam from the boiler. Patterson received a shock, in fact an electric shock. Armstrong became intrigued and started to investigate the phenomenon. Within a year he had produced a paper on 'The Electricity of Effluent Steam' which he read to the Literary and Philosophical Society of Newcastle. From there he went on to produce, with his friend Watson, a hydro-electric machine using high power steam. Essentially, this was a boiler, properly insulated, from which steam escaped at high pressure through specially constructed nozzles. He demonstrated it to a packed audience at the 'Lit and Phil', so packed in fact that he himself could not get through the auditorium on to the stage. Instead he had to enter like a burglar from a window in the rear.

The hydro-electric machine represented the most effective way of generating electricity and indeed remained a viable concept for over fifty years. Some of the foremost engineers in the country, like Faraday and Wheatstone, now came to hear of his work. They proposed that the Royal Society should elect him a Fellow and this was done.

John Wigham Richardson, who was to become a famous

Tyneside shipbuilder, remembered seeing Armstrong demonstrate his machine. 'One dark night in the Christmas holidays,' he wrote in his autobiography, 'our father took us four elder children to see Lord Armstrong (then Mr William George Armstrong, solicitor) exhibit his electrical machine ... It was a weird scene; the sparks or flashes of electricity from the machine were, I should say, from four to five feet long and the figure of Armstrong in a frock coat (since then so familiar) looked almost demoniacal.'[3]

To become an F.R.S. was a great distinction for someone who was still a practising solicitor. But the day was now drawing near when William Armstrong's hobby and career would become one. At the beginning of 1845 the Whittle Dene Water Company was formed in Newcastle.

## THE WHITTLE DENE WATER COMPANY

The prospectus, published early in 1845, declared: 'There are few advantages which a large and populous town can possess more important than a copious supply of water, suitable alike for drinking and for general domestic purposes. Not only is it essential to the health, comfort and convenience of the inhabitants at large but it is conducive, in the highest degree, to habits of sobriety and cleanliness in the working classes, especially when it is conveyed into their own houses and supplied at all times without restriction. The benefits, however, which an abundance of good water are calculated to confer, have never yet been extended to the towns of Newcastle and Gateshead, and so loud and universal are now the complaints of the bad quality of the water obtained from the river Tyne for the use of the inhabitants that there is every inducement to seek elsewhere for a purer source of supply than that river is capable of affording ... The smaller streams which occur in the immediate vicinity of Newcastle and Gateshead are all either deficient in quantity or defective in the quality of the water ... Fortunately, however, there exists, within a practicable distance of Newcastle, a stream called Whittle Burn, which is situated in the neighbourhood of Ovingham and is free from all these objections and a project has recently been formed for obtaining from that source the much-needed supply of pure water.'

The intended company contained the names of some prominent local people, including the Mayor, Mr Addison Potter. The solicitors were Donkin, Stable and Armstrong and, indeed, according to a contemporary document, 'the master mind who directed the movement was that of Mr William George Armstrong whose hydraulic inventions were just beginning to attract attention'.

The capital of the company was £120,000 and its intention was to build a reservoir where a number of streams joined forces about a mile North West of the village of Horsley in Northumberland. From there the water would flow along pipes through Wylam, Newburn and Lemington to Newcastle, and Gateshead. The water would be supplied into every house without the expensive individual pumping system then needed. This would mean that instead of only ten per cent of the population having a direct water supply, virtually everyone would have one.

The committee of the proposed company approached the Duke of Northumberland for permission to use his land. The Duke's agent wrote to Newcastle Council on 1st January 1845 : 'So far as the comfort of the inhabitants or the sanitary condition of the town is concerned his Grace conceives that such a proposal would meet with universal approbation; but residing at some distance, it is possible objections may exist unknown to his Grace. If, therefore, the Mayor and the Corporation of Newcastle, who, as a public body, are not only capable of judging but anxious to promote the general welfare, would oblige his Grace by stating that the measure would be satisfactory, if carried, it will give his Grace much pleasure to render his assistance in the manner required.'

The letter was referred to the Town Improvement Committee. On 12th February, after interviewing Armstrong separately and later the other members, the Town Improvement Committee expressed 'to the Council our opinion that the project of the Whittle Dene Water Company is likely to be beneficial to the town'. There were opponents, however.

Mr Edward Hall wanted the council to set up a Special Committee to look into the question for he feared the creation of a monopoly supplier of water. The council 'should take care that the public were not charged too much for water'.

Alderman Armorer Donkin pointed out that the prospective company had announced its prices and Sir John Fife said he thought they should have received the proposal with enthusiasm. Mr Armstrong senior entered into the debate. He thought that neither the prices nor the details were subjects for the council's concern. They simply had to decide whether the supplying of the town with this water would be beneficial or the contrary. Assuming the water was pure, it followed that an abundant supply of it would benefit the town. That was all that needed to be communicated to the Duke. The details they would have a chance of considering when the bill was put before Parliament.

However a majority of the council thought a special committee should be set up to consider the whole question of the town's future water supply. By August, its report was ready. It said the scheme was satisfactory. On the question of prices, 'the promoters of the bill readily consented to insert in their Act a reduced and regularly-graduated scale, which appears, on the whole, to be moderate and fair'. The Council approved the scheme. Perhaps they could not do anything else since Parliament had passed the bill in June 1845 and construction work was going ahead. The Whittle Dene Water Company became the Newcastle and Gateshead Water Company in 1863.

Before then it constructed six large reservoirs holding 215 million gallons in Whittle Dene where the water of the Whittle Burn was collected by damming. At the first meeting of the shareholders in July 1845 it was decided that Armstrong should be appointed secretary at a salary of £150 a year. He held the position until 11th February 1847 when a minute of the company reported the directors' regret that Armstrong had decided to tender his resignation because he had new commitments.

But he retained a life-long interest in the Whittle Dene Water Company. On the death of Mr A. L. Potter in 1854 he was elected chairman. He held the office until 1867 and it was during his chairmanship that it developed into the Newcastle and Gateshead Water Company. However, in 1847 the fateful turning point had arrived for Armstrong. To see how, let us go back to November 1845, just after the Whittle Dene Water Company had been set up and Armstrong had been made secretary.

## THE HYDRAULIC CRANE

On 24th November 1845 he wrote the following letter to the Finance Committee of the Town Council.

'Gentlemen,

I beg to draw your attention to a plan I have matured for applying the pressure of the water in the streets' pipes in the lower parts of Newcastle, to the working of the cranes upon the Quay, with the view of increasing the rapidity and lessening the expense of the operation of delivering ships.

It will readily be perceived that whatever has a tendency to accelerate the unloading of ships at the Quay must not only be highly advantageous to the shipowners and merchants of the port, but must also have the effect of increasing the accommodation to shipping which the Quay is now capable of affording.

A working model has been constructed for the purpose of illustrating the operation of a crane upon the proposed plan; and I am fully persuaded, after a careful investigation of the subject, that the advantages to which I have adverted would be realized by such a method of lifting goods.

In order to relieve the Corporation from the speculative outlet of making the experiment upon a large scale, a few of my friends are willing to join me in the risk and expense of adapting the plan to one of the existing cranes; provided that should the experiment prove successful a lease be granted to us of all the cranes upon the Quay belonging to the Corporation for the period of ten years, at the present rate and upon the following terms and conditions.

Ist. That we shall be at liberty to apply the hydraulic principle to all the existing cranes, and shall have the exclusive right of erecting others on the same principle upon the Quay in situations to be approved of by the Corporation or their authorized agent.

2nd. That we shall be bound to reduce the present rates of

W.G. Armstrong aged 20, painting by Ramsay.

W.G. Armstrong and friends.

cranage to the extent of at least 20%.

3rd. That the Corporation shall take the machinery at a valuation at the end of the term.

We will also engage, in case the experiment should fail, to restore the crane to be operated upon to its present state, if required.

Should you think proper to accede to this proposition and the result of the trial should be favourable, the public and the port will reap the immediate advantage of the improved system, and the Corporation will eventually come into the receipt of an increased revenue, without sustaining any loss in the meantime.

> I am Gentlemen,
> Your very obedient servant,
> (signed) W. G. Armstrong.'

The Finance Committee were impressed by the scheme and sent it forward to the full council for ratification. They did feel, however, that a number of further conditions should apply.

They thought Armstrong should be obliged to erect from time to time, during the ten years, such new cranes as the council required. Those erected during the first three years should be paid for entirely by Armstrong. During the rest of the period the Council should 'bear a fair proportion of the cost' of any other cranes that were needed. In estimating the amount 'due regard should be had to the prospect of Mr Armstrong being remunerated for his outlay'.

The Town Clerk, John Clayton, read the letter together with the Finance Committee's recommendations to a full meeting of the council on Wednesday, 14th January 1846, a meeting attended, of course, by Armstrong senior as a councillor. Alderman James Hodgson, chairman of the Finance Committee, said that 'if no gentleman saw any objection, he would move the confirmation of the report. The terms of the agreement would be afterwards laid before them. He considered it an ingenious discovery and one that deserved the approbation of the Council'.

There was no dissent. How could there be? As Alderman Hodgson went on to say: 'If any difference of opinion arose as to the success of the operation, it would be submitted to reference. The Corporation would be safe whether the experiment succeeded or not.'

The Mayor, Alderman Thomas Headlam, said he 'could also bear testimony to the ingenuity of the experiment, and to the successful action of the model upon a small scale. It appeared the Corporation could suffer no loss and the port would immediately receive the benefit of diminished expense in the unloading of ships'.

The proposal was accepted unanimously. The trial was little more than a formality and the lease of the cranage was granted. Armstrong, now 35 years of age, was finally entering the world of manufacture. With him went four of his associates from the water company. There was Armorer Donkin, his old friend and mentor, Addison Potter, a leading public figure, George Cruddas, an expert on finance, and Richard Lambert, another old friend whom Armstrong had first met when they were both studying in London. These five formed a small company called the Newcastle Cranage Company. A year later they were to join together to form Messrs W. G. Armstrong and Company.

At first the company ran into some opposition. There were some unpleasant remarks at the Water Company's shareholders meeting in February 1847. Some of the shareholders clearly thought that a small clique of directors was using the water supply for their own ends and for their own private profit. There were complaints that the crane used too much water and that the price asked was too low. Both Armstrong and Cruddas had to come to the defence of the Cranage Company.

This little local difficulty was soon overcome. By November 1846 Armstrong was able to tell the Town Clerk that the crane 'having now been sufficiently tested to render its permanent success a matter of certainty, I shall feel obliged by your informing the council that I am prepared to carry out my agreement by erection of additional cranes of the same description.'[4] In fact, he planned to use another four but only three were installed. They were built at Watson's works.

In the same letter quoted above Armstrong outlined a plan for expediting the movement of cargo. 'The general stoppage and confusion which attend the unloading of vessels upon the quay; the accumulation of goods and crush of carts around the cranes; and the exposure of valuable merchandise to the frequent inclemency of the weather, are all to be attributed to the absence of adjacent depots and warehouses, where goods might be received direct from the ship and where they might be weighed, gauged, marked and sorted without obstructing the process of delivery.' He also proposed trams, driven by water power to move the goods from the quayside into the depots and then the use of trains to take them from the depots to their destinations.

Armstrong urged the council to implement his plan quickly. 'If, however, the Corporation should decline the undertaking upon the ground of its speculative character, or from any other cause, I am in a position to say that I shall be able to carry it into execution as a private enterprise.' He did not say where the funds were to come from. But in any case his mind was now turning in another direction, the creation of his own works. The other partners agreed that there was a commercial asset to exploit in Armstrong's patents and that the best way to do so would be to set up their own factory. On 1st January 1847 a partnership was formed to implement this plan.

In February 1847 Armstrong resigned both from the secretaryship of the Whittle Dene Water Company and from his legal practice. Looking back years later he said: 'When, at length, I resolved, about 1847, to give up my profession and start in business as a mechanical engineer, most of my friends thought I was very foolish. And on the face of it, it was a bold thing to do—abandoning, for an entirely new enterprise, the large and old-established legal business which, in the course of time, would become my own.'

Perhaps. But at last, at the age of 37, he was free to follow his own impulse. For fifteen years he had swung 'like an erratic pendulum between the law office and the lathe'. At last he had made the choice that he knew he should. He had given up a safe, remunerative but essentially boring occupation for a speculative, demanding but enticing one. Of course, if all failed, he could go back to the law. But he had decided that his pendulum-like life must stop. It was in his nature that it should. His life so far had been frustrating, not only because he could not follow his real interest but also because he kept moving from one subject to another. It was only now that he had at last made the choice that perhaps his prime characteristic was to get a chance to express itself: an intense, unshakeable ability to concentrate. It was this quality above all that was to turn a man noted as a local dilettante into a national hero.

# CHAPTER TWO

## INDUSTRY IN BRITAIN

THE 1840's and 1850's were years of rapid and dramatic changes. New factories sprang up everywhere and new towns around them. Industrialisation seemed to surge and throb through Britain. As it did so, it destroyed the feudal way of life. The proud, independent, craftsmen were to become wage labourers in the factories and suffer humiliation and privation, such as they had never known before. J. D. Bernal wrote in his *Science in History*:

'All economic and political initiative belonged to the new class of capitalist entrepreneurs ... Wealth had never been accumulated so easily; misery had never been so widespread and unmitigated by social defences. With all the new triumphs of engineering went a smoky dirtiness, drabness and ugliness which no previous civilization could have produced.'[1]

These were the years when the railways spread throughout the country. Nearly all the main lines were laid at this time while the enterprise of George Hudson, 'The Railway King', and others led to the consolidation of local branches into great trunk systems. In turn, the rapid development of the railways created a rising demand for iron. Numerous works opened in County Durham. Two were particularly important. In 1841 the Consett Iron Works were established and 'what had once been a barren moor without population for miles around speedily became an immense hive of industry'.[2] Four years later, in 1845, the Witton Park Ironworks were opened in Bishop Auckland.

The growth of the iron smelting industry was as nothing compared with what was happening in coal production. The whole of the eastern part of County Durham was starting to be exploited. The coal seams were deeper here than in the west but very rich once they were reached. Sometimes it took years to reach them. The Bensham seam near Monkwearmouth at Sunderland was opened up only after eight years of digging and the investment of £80,000 to £100,000 by the proprietors. The Hutton seam at Murton was even more expensive to reach. A total expenditure of more than £250,000 was needed.

The conditions for the men, women and children who worked in the mines were appalling. Take as an example George Hall. He went to work as a child of eight in 1842. He damaged his skull by falling against the crane handle when he was too tired to stand up. He was away from work for six months. When he returned, he was involved in another accident which broke his thigh. All this before he was ten years of age. It was not the case that he was accident-prone. It was difficult to avoid accidents when you were working for twelve hours in almost total darkness hundreds of feet under the earth.

Domestic conditions were hardly any better. There was dreadful overcrowding in the towns. Sanitary conveniences were virtually non-existent, certainly for the poor. Filth was thrown into the streets. Drainage was almost unknown. In such conditions, the risk of disease and of epidemics was a real and obvious one. Even in the new towns, like Middlesbrough, or in the new parts of old towns conditions were little better. Social provision remained primitive, conservative and backward at a time when technology was making vast strides.

Nowhere was this new era more noticeable than in the emergence of the mechanical engineer. 'The appearance of the modern engineer was a new social phenomenon', wrote Bernal in the book quoted above. 'He is not the lineal descendant of the old military engineer but rather of the millwright and the metal-worker of the days of craftsmanship.'[3]

There were numerous, now famous, examples: Maudsley, Whitworth, the Stephensons, the Brunels and, of course, for our purpose William George Armstrong.

THE BEGINNING OF ELSWICK

When Armstrong took the vital decision to leave the law and set up as a manufacturer he was not alone. Four of his friends, all on the board of the Whittle Dene Water Company, came with him. It is difficult now to say whether he persuaded them to form a company or they persuaded him. Perhaps it was a little of both. Their influence on him certainly outweighed that of his father who wanted him to stay put.

One of Armstrong's friends, Lord Stuart Rendel, looking back sixty years later, wrote: 'Naturally, Lord Armstrong's father disliked the idea of his son deserting an excellent and a perfectly secure career for what he deemed an inferior as well as a more precarious career as a mechanical engineer, nor was there in Lord Armstrong's character any turn for manufacturing enterprise. My father (James Meadows Rendel) was so enthusiastic as to the future of the application of water power upon the methods illustrated by the Armstrong cranes that he took a step that settled the question. He told Lord Armstrong and his father that if his invention was to receive effective development, Lord Armstrong must himself take in hand the manufacture and set up suitable works. He said he could not help him with money, as he considered that he ought to have no money interest in the enterprise, but he promised immediate orders sufficient to keep a moderate factory employed. As my father was the leading hydraulic engineer of the country, this promise amounted to a guarantee on which Lord Armstrong, though without money support from his father, could collect the requisite means.'[4]

So it proved. Addison Potter, Armorer Donkin, George Cruddas and Richard Lambert, all of whom were associated with Armstrong in the Whittle Dene Water Company, decided to back him. The five men formed a partnership on 1st January 1847. Potter, Donkin, and Cruddas each put up £5,000. Cruddas also put up another £2,500 to buy a half share for Lambert, who had no spare capital at that time. He was an old friend of Armstrong's—indeed they had studied law together—and a popular figure with all the other partners. It was felt that he should be one of them. Armstrong himself put up £2,000 in cash while his patents were valued at £3,000. So the original company was founded with a capital of £22,000 of which just under £20,000 was cash.

Within a few years, two of the original pioneers were dead. Donkin died in 1851, leaving his share to Armstrong in his will. Potter died in 1854. His share was bought by the three remaining partners from trustees. Neither Donkin nor Potter played an active role in the early days of the company. They were, after all, old men even in 1847. Richard Lambert did not play a positive role either. The responsibility fell on Armstrong and Cruddas. And a heavy one it was. One reads of them working unceasingly and tirelessly for the success of their little company. It was quite plainly upon their efforts that any hopes for the future lay.

Looking back years later, Armstrong said: 'I have worked hard in my time. For the first fifteen years after starting the works at Elswick, you know, I had a very hard struggle to make headway. During the whole of that time I never had a week's holiday and many a night I stayed at Elswick all night, working on till ten or eleven when I had some important matter in hand, and then laying down on a couch for a few hours ... At times I suffered from the inventor's fever, I suppose, and got little sleep at night in consequence. But that would be only when I was at the crisis of important experiments. I have always lived regularly and temperately however.'[5]

The first requirement after the legal formation of the company was the purchase of land on which to build a factory. Within a few days the partners had decided that they would look westward. There they found a site at Elswick which offered conspicious advantages: ample space for development; and good communication links by both road and rail. The site consisted of five and a half acres situated at the western end of the Estate of Elswick near to a village called Scotswood.

It had been in the hands of the Hodgson family since 1720. The present owner, John Hodgson Hinde, was an energetic man who had represented the City in Parliament for some years. He took a great interest in his estate. He built the Scotswood Road through it to link with the Suspension Bridge at Scotswood that was opened in 1831. And he did not object, as landowners did in other areas, when the Newcastle and Carlisle Railway Company asked if they could build a branch line from Blaydon, on the south bank, across the river and through his land to Newcastle. It was mainly the presence of both road and rail links that attracted the new partners.

They also appreciated the advantages offered by the river. At this time, of course, it was undredged. The Tyne Commissioners were not to come into existence for another three years; the effect of their work would not be noticeable for another ten. There were in fact two large islands opposite the potential site for the factory. But no matter. The river was navigable. There was a flat area to be built upon between the river and the railway. There was room for expansion. Newcastle was just two miles away yet land prices were considerably less here than in the City. Elswick it was to be.

A revolution was about to begin. An account written in 1901 said: 'The Elswick of sixty years ago was ... considered to be a spot of great natural beauty, with green fields sloping pleasantly from the heights of Benwell to the river Tyne ... The Elswick Works were reached by a country walk along the Scotswood Road. Little enjoyment of the picturesque is to be derived from the same pilgrimage today for Elswick has stretched towards the town and the town towards Elswick until the whole locality is now a dingy labyrinth of closely-packed houses and streets. Much as the face of the soil has been altered, the river has been even more changed. It now flows past the works in a broad current and has been so effectively dredged that ships drawing twenty-five feet of water can come under the sheer legs of the east end of the Ordnance Department. But until comparatively recent years there was in mid-stream, exactly opposite the present offices, a large island where was "The Countess of Coventry" Inn, and where, as living witnesses testify, horse races and athletic sports of all kinds were once held. Another feature of the neighbourhood was the abundance of game to be found in its meadows and hedgerows and even in the opening days of the works partridges and pheasants were occasionally seen within the boundary wall. The Metropolitan sportsman who remembered shooting a woodcock on the site of the Marble Arch has his parallel at Elswick in a veteran who, as an apprentice, joined in the pursuit of a hare where the present bridge yard stands, a spot which today scarcely suggests ground game.'[6]

The partners bought five and a half acres for £5,500 and signed the deeds of conveyance on 10th April 1847. The payment, the first made by the new company, was in two parts, A cheque for £3,988 10s. 0d. was given to John Hodgson Hinde and another for £498 16s. 9d. went to the Newcastle builder Richard Grainger. Probably he had a mortgage on the property. The final payment for the remaining £1,000 was made in October.

Building work started immediately. By May one reads of Armstrong signing a bill for materials; common wallers 8d. a horse load; quarry blockers 2s. a horse load; ordinary blockers 3d. a foot; leading 10d. a horse load.

### THE FACTORY

Three main buildings were put up: a machinery shop, a blacksmiths shop and an erecting shop, with a joiners and patternmakers section at one end. There was also a small two-storey building for an office. Mr Cruddas would have the accounts department on the ground floor while the offices of Armstrong and the Drawing Department would be upstairs. Six houses, called Foremen's Row, were put up at the western edge of the factory site. They no doubt helped to attract some good men to the works and they could be called upon at any hour of the day or night.

Meanwhile Armstrong had opened an office at 10 Hood Street in the centre of Newcastle to deal with correspondence. A few orders were coming in already even before any machinery had been bought. That was the next priority then. Soon requests for information were going out to leading machine tool makers. By a strange coincidence the very first letter sent out by the new company went to Messrs Whitworth and Company of Manchester. It was an enquiry for a lathe. A few years later William Armstrong and Sir Joseph Whitworth were to become fierce protagonists in the 'battle of the guns', a struggle to win Government contracts. Many years after that, towards the end of the century, the two firms, forgetting their former enmity, were to combine. Other enquiries were also sent out.

The orders followed: nine machines from Smith, Beacock and Tannett, eight from Buckton and Company, eight from Joseph and James Fox, seven from Lawson and Sons, six from Andrew Shanks. About 50 machines were ordered in quick succession yet still they were not enough. But money was flowing out quickly.

Throughout that first summer the partners became increasingly anxious about finance. They had put up £19,500 in cash in January. It had disappeared fast. The land cost £5,500, the buildings £15,000, the machines £14,000. With other outgoings, capital expenditure in the first few months came to £36,000. This might have been a moment for panic. Instead two of them—Donkin and Cruddas—agreed to raise their stake by another £7,000 between them. They also were largely responsible for raising £17,000 from outside loans at five per cent interest. The capital of the company was now £43,000. That offered a breathing space.

Production was soon to start and as the orders were completed and despatched, perhaps payments would start flowing in. During the summer some of the main appointments were made. Armstrong persuaded George Hutchinson to leave Watson's High Bridge Works, where they had met, and come to work for him as his assistant. Hutchinson was regarded, in fact, as Armstrong's second in command. The works manager was to be Henry Thompson, also imported from Watson's. A Mr Windlow and a Mr Singleton were to be in charge of the machine shop. The smithy was to be under the charge of James Dowell, who came to the company in June from Robert Stephenson and Co.

One or two workmen were also taken on during the summer. There was a young man called George Bonner who, with his father, applied for work while Armstrong was still using his office in Hood Street. They helped to erect some of the workshops. They also started on some of the early contracts before the shops had roofs on. George Bonner remembered even into his old age working at a bench in an open field.

Although a few men were taken on in this way, Armstrong was keen to train his own labour force. In September he indentured six apprentices. They started work at six o'clock on the morning of September 20th. One of them saw the new boss even before arriving at the factory. Young Robert Mills was making his way to the new premises in the early autumn light when he saw Mr Armstrong at the bottom of Glue Factory Lane driving in a phaeton pulled by a white pony.

Even then, in late September, the factory was unfinished although some of the machines were in the machine shop. It was still unfinished by the following month. But even so it was officially declared ready for business. The first wages bill for manufacturing was paid on 15th October and came to £9 17s. 6d. Two months later, the wages bill was up to £42, indicating that about 20 men were on the books. Another 100 or so were still working on completing the buildings and installing the machinery.

## THE FIRST ORDERS

The factory began production in October on four 12-ton cranes, number 6 to 9, for the Edinburgh and Northern Railway. The cranes were needed to lift loaded carriages weighing ten tons each, from the Firth of Forth ferry boat to the railway for the rest of the journey. The operation was to take no longer than a minute per carriage. Apparently it was not possible to use a natural head of water so power had to be supplied by a six horse power steam engine which could pump water continuously into a tank 180 feet high.

Armstrong quoted for the work on 11th August 1847 and gave a price of £3,800. The tender was accepted and the work became the first production job for the new factory. The delivery date was the first of March 1848. But when that day arrived, the new company, which was naturally anxious to receive its first income, found that the railway directors had changed their minds. They did not want Armstrong's cranes.

The company insisted they should take them. On 1st March Armstrong wrote a letter to the Edinburgh and Northern Railway Company pointing out that half the contract amount was due since the cranes were completed. There was no reply. Armstrong wrote again. After a long tussle the railway company finally agreed to take the cranes but refused to pay for them in cash. Instead, it offered debentures in the railway. It was all a sad lesson for the new company which wanted to start paying off the £17,000 loans, costing £850 a year in interest, as soon as it possibly could.

Happily there was no difficulty with another early contract. Armstrong himself used to recall that this was the first order for the new company although actual production work started a week or two after the railway contract. Armstrong told the story in this way:

'Amongst others the late Sir William Cubitt (then Mr Cubitt) took a very early interest in the machine (the hydraulic crane) and wrote to Mr Jesse Hartley, who was then the engineer of the Liverpool Docks, urging him to go and see it, but that somewhat eccentric gentleman, who was very averse to novelties, at first flatly refused to do so. A second letter from Sir William Cubitt put the matter in such a light that Mr Hartley could not persist in his refusal without incurring the imputation of shutting his eyes to improvements; so without giving any notice of his intention he went to Newcastle alone to see the crane. It was not at work when he arrived but the man in charge was there and Mr Hartley entered into a bantering conversation with him. This man, who went by the name of "Hydraulic Jack", had acquired great dexterity in the management of the machine and being put upon his "mettle" by Mr Hartley's incredulous observations, he proceeded to show its action by a daring treatment of a hogshead of sugar. He began by running it up with great velocity to the head of the jib, and then letting it as rapidly descend, but by gradually reducing its speed as it neared the ground he stopped it softly before it quite touched the pavement. He next swung it round to the opposite side of the circle, continuing to lift and lower with great rapidity, while the jib was in motion and, in short, he exhibited the machine to such advantage that Mr Hartley's prejudices were vanquished. Mr Hartley, who will be remembered as a man whose odd ways were combined with a frank and generous disposition, displayed no feeling of discomforture but at once called upon the author whom he laconically addressed in the following words: "I am Jesse Hartley of Liverpool and I have seen your crane. It is the very thing I want, and I shall recommend its adoption at the Albert Dock." With scarcely another word he bade adieu and returned to Liverpool. This anecdote marks an epoch in the history of hydraulic cranes which then passed from the stage of experiment to that of assured adoption.'[7]

The Albert Docks took two warehouse lifts, costing £1,000 the pair, and paid W. G. Armstrong and Company by cheque on 15th May 1848, this being the new company's first revenue from sales.

## MORE CRANE ORDERS

Crane No. 10 was ordered for Glasgow New Harbour. Then in 1848 the company won a large contract for hydraulic machinery for the lead mines at Allenheads in Northumberland. Other work was done in these early days for coal mines. It did not always meet with the aproval of the miners. In the winter of 1849 George Henderson, the head of the drawing office, went to the South Hetton colliery in South Durham to supervise the erection of some Armstrong machinery. The weather was bleak, with deep snow and a biting wind. An outbreak of cholera was just beginning to die down after raging through the locality. To make things even worse, the men were intensely resentful of the new machinery. Henderson was in such circumstances anything but a welcome visitor. In fact, hostility became so strong that the village doctor used to walk Henderson back to his lodgings in case he might be attacked. He was not. But the machinery was. For some time, there was a comic though serious set of incidents, with Henderson mending the machinery and the men breaking it again. Finally, it was decided not to use it until the men's feelings had died down.

Elsewhere, Elswick products were greeted enthusiastically. Within the first four years various railway companies placed many orders: York, Newcastle and Berwick Railway ordered 17 cranes; the York and North Midland 8; the Manchester, Sheffield and Lincoln 30; the Great Northern 35 and the Great Western 16. In addition, the Regents Canal Company placed orders for 24 and the Birkenhead Dock for 12.

Two individuals were particularly impressed: Isambard Kingdom Brunel placed many contracts; so did James Rendel as he promised he would. All these orders for cranes were gained in the first four years and meant a considerable amount of work for the new company. Many other orders came in for hydraulic machinery of different kinds. For example, Armstrong adapted his system to the working of dock gates and this brought new orders. One of the most significant was from Mr

Rendel for gates for the Great Grimsby Docks. The contract was worth £13,487, by far the largest the company had received.

About this time Armstrong began to consider a major modification to his system. It led to a far greater number of uses. His original concept was to exploit the power that ran to waste in the many natural heads of water in the country. Since then, he had adapted the system to overcome the obvious disadvantage that natural water power was not always available where it was wanted. In such circumstances, he advised the building of a tall tower into which a steam engine pumped the necessary supply of water. But even this was not the final answer, for it was not always possible to build high water towers. This was the case at New Holland on the Humber. The Manchester, Sheffield and Lincoln Railway had ordered five 2-ton cranes to be erected there in 1850. But the foundations at New Holland consisted mostly of sand. A high water tower could not be erected.

For many weeks, Armstrong puzzled over what to do. He worked late, combining the role of scientific researcher with that of manufacturer. Many nights he slept in his office on the small camp bed he kept there. Finally, he arrived at a solution, a device now known universally as an 'accumulator'.

The accumulator consisted of a large cast-iron cylinder fitted with a loaded plunger to give pressure to the water injected by the engine. This enabled the pressure to be pushed up from 90 lbs. a square inch to 600 lbs. The higher pressure allowed distribution pipes to be made of smaller dimensions. The invention also widened enormously the range of applications for hydraulic machinery. It became particularly useful for all manner of cranes, hoists and lifts, dock gates and ships. In fact, without it the warships that were to emerge in the second half of the nineteenth century would have been an impossibility.

Armstrong continued to improve his hydraulic machinery over many years, taking out a third patent in 1856. For this side of his work, Cambridge University made him an honorary Doctor of Laws in 1862 and Oxford University made him a Doctor of Civil Law in 1870. The Society of Arts also gave him their Albert Medal 'because of his distinction as an engineer and as a scientific man and because by the development of the transmission of power hydraulically, due to his constant efforts extending over many years, the manufacturers of this country have been greatly aided and mechanical power beneficially substituted for most laborious and injurious labour'.

## THE FACTORY GROWS

The development of the accumulator opened up the possibility of using hydraulic power universally. There followed a substantial increase in the orders for cranes and other machinery. The small company began in fact to bulge with orders.

In that year, 1850, the company turned out 45 cranes. Within two years the number had shot up to 75. It was to go even higher, to an average of a hundred cranes a year, an average that persisted until the turn of the century when sales faded away. But throughout the whole of the second half of the nineteenth century sales of hydraulic cranes averaged two a week although with dramatic peaks and troughs. In 1864 the actual figure was 212 cranes. In 1869 it was 75. The variations in output generally coincided with the general economic situation in the country. Over the ninety years of production, from 1847 to 1936, a total of 5,382 cranes were made. In the early years, the railway companies were the most important customers. The share of output taken by them rose to a peak in 1875 and then declined, as the overall growth of railways began to decline. Docks and harbours continued to take a steady fifth of production but a new market had to be found to replace the railways and the company sought its new customers abroad. In fact, the commercial development of the Colonies made them a natural market.

The export share of output rose from a quarter in 1860 to sixty per cent by the turn of the century. The production of hydraulic cranes continued throughout Armstrong's life to be a sound bread-and-butter business, a business that became firmly established in 1850 with the sudden spurt of orders.

More men were taken on to cope with the demand. More buildings were needed to house the men and more machines

W.G. Armstrong in old age.

Armstrong and his favourite dogs outside the front door at
Cragside.

for them to use. The fledgling company, started only a couple of years before, was learning to fly very quickly.

By 1850 over 300 men were employed and the number was continuing to rise all the time. The years 1850 and 1851 were particularly good ones with numerous orders from railway companies. Armstrong's ambitions grew even faster than the firm, however. For he was determined from the outset that the company should expand into a general engineering concern, rather than a specialist manufacturer of hydraulic machinery. He branched out into bridge building. One of the first essays, the Inverness Bridge, which was completed in June 1855, proved to be an unprofitable contract. In fact, heavy losses were made. Even so, the firm went ahead and tendered for the Soane Bridge. This was a much bigger bridge, ordered by the East India Railway Company, and brought the company a very nice profit.

The same could not be said for locomotive manufacture, another activity into which the new company tried to diversify. Railways were then spreading all over the country. There was a railway boom. Not unnaturally it was a development that caught Armstrong's fancy and he produced a novel model, called the 'Flying Dutchman'. Armstrong's object was to increase power by means of a condenser. His concept was ingenious but required a constant supply of cold water, a difficulty that proved insurmountable.

In any case, novelty of design was not now looked for. By the early 1850's standard designs were monopolizing the market. If the firm had really wanted to break into this new sphere of operation, a more conventional design would have provided a greater chance. As it was, the Flying Dutchman, which cost about £2,000 to build, attracted no buyers. Later, it was broken up and some of the parts used in other engines.

These early attempts at diversification cost the company rather dear. For they prevented it from producing a profit as quickly as it might have done. The research and development costs in fact more than offset the first two years' profits of £968 and £911 respectively, which were made on the hydraulic side of the business. They also delayed the day when the partners would receive a dividend. In fact, both Donkin and Potter were dead before the first dividend was distributed in

March 1854. It was five per cent dividend for the year 1853 and the amount actually paid out was £1,075. Of course, by this time the initial debt of £17,000 had been cleared off. The long wait before the first dividend might have been another indication of the financial caution and prudence exercised by George Cruddas, with the agreement of the partners. It seems that they agreed to pump as much of the profits as they could back into the business. In this way, the capital account increased from £20,00 in 1847 to nearly £100,000 by 1862, a fivefold increase in fifteen years.

FINANCIAL PROBLEMS

W. G. Armstrong and Company's first cash book dates from 5th April 1847. On that day, £5,000 was taken from the 'Private Ledger' which contained details of the capital account, and was paid into the Northumberland and Durham District Bank. On 10th April, payments of £4,500 were made to Hodgson, Hinde and Grainger for land. On 14th another £2,000 was transferred from the capital account to the current account and on the 22nd a further £6,000 was similarly transferred.

Apart from land, other payments in the first month were mostly for building work. Mr William Graydon, the building inspector, was paid £6 1s. 4d. 'Mr Ralph Gardener and other joiners at the workshops' were paid £2 16s. 9d. Mr Robert Airey, labourer at roadmaking received £2 7s. 6d. Other expenses in that first month included £5 for damage to gardens, £1 for writing paper, £4 6s. 3d. for instruments for the office and £4 10s. 6d. for ropes. Only 15s. was left to carry forward to the next month so that at the beginning of May the transfer of another £2,000 from capital account was needed. No wonder an increase in capital was required, as related earlier.

But the company's success in winning orders pulled it through. The achievement was the more remarkable in that the late forties were a difficult time for the engineering industry in general. For example, Hawthorns had to reduce their labour force from over 1,000 in 1847 to 850 two years later. The depression continued into the early 1850's. In 1851-52, the number of engineering workers who were unemployed exceeded ten per cent. But Armstrong's factory seemed isolated from these general conditions. It continued to grow rapidly. By March 1852, just five years after buying the land, about 350 men were employed and the amount paid for a fortnight's wages was £870, about 25s. a week.

William Armstrong was becoming established as an important Tyneside employer. His name began to appear in the newspapers more frequently, sometimes in a critical light. At about this time, for example, the *Northern Examiner* declared:

'He should build cottages for his men ... His workmen are either scattered throughout the town, from which they come in swarms, along the road in the darkness of the wintry morning or they are forced to inhabit the pestilential cribs of such places as Greenhow Terrace—a place from its nastiness and filth, fatal to many a man and woman ... Mr Armstrong's example would tell on the whole district and tend to promote that kindness and co-operation which is so necessary for the peace and comfort of employer and employed. He is surely the very man to realize our notions for a model cottage.'

The newspapers' hopes were not fulfilled. Newcastle was too convenient for Armstrong to need to bother, at least for the moment.

But while he was unsympathetic in this direction he was more liberal in others. John Winlow and some other workers from Armstrong's established the Elswick Mechanics Institute shortly after the works began. The company provided a library with eventually 2,000 volumes and a reading room. A contemporary account described Armstrong's library as ' a testimony to his care and anxiety to throw open the portals of literature and science to the working classes'. The technical staff provided instruction courses and these were recognized as avenues for promotion from the works to the office staff. Later, Armstrong was to spread this concept to schoolchildren by providing schools for his workmen's children. The Elswick school was opened in 1866 and was financed by 'a tax of only 2d. a week on the higher paid men and of 1d on those who received lower wages'. The firm erected school buildings and a management committee was set up, composed of representatives of the firm and of the men. The school became the second largest in the city and was not absorbed by the local authority until this century. The staff and children at the school as well as members of the Mechanics Institute were apparently regularly entertained at the Armstrong home.

The school log book for 1869 showed the school soon settled down under the headmaster, Mr George Hill, and the four assistant teachers. One reads entries like the following:

10 May   Another wet morning; always unfavourable for numbers coming up, especially a Monday morning. Lessons very well prepared. P.M. A good attendance. All went on steadily.

12 May   Passed 14 boys from 4th to 3rd Class. Lessons very well prepared. Had a short visit from Mr Rowell. Usual progress in the Classes.

24 May   A good attendance. Home lessons very well prepared. Usual progress in the classes. Had a visit from Mr Rowell.

In the summer, when the examinations were held, the results were:

Average attendance for past year—266
Number presented—222
No. passed in reading—218
   ,,        ,,        writing—211
   ,,        ,,        arithmetic—197

H.M. Inspector of Schools, H. E. Oakeley, made this comment after visiting the school: 'In the boys school, the class rooms are too small; in other respects, the premises are very good. The Master shewed great intelligence in presenting the boys for examination, having previously been unacquainted with the Government system and the results were remarkably good. The boys are very orderly and the discipline is good.'

No doubt the solid progress made by the teachers prompted the school committee to increase the teachers' wages. On 16th June, there is an entry: 'Mr Rycroft (secretary to the committee) gave notice of the following advances of salaries: viz: Head Master 10 £ per annum, Mr McIlwraith 5 £ per annum, Mr Fenwick 5 £ per annum, Tho. J. Laverick and Wm. Telford 2s. per week each.'

By 1875 the average attendance had risen to 386. The salary of the Head Master was increased from £200 to £230 a year with corresponding rises for the other five teachers.

This is taking our story a long way forward. Let us go back twenty years to see how a fundamental change occurred in the fortunes of Armstrong and his firm.

In 1854 the outbreak of the Crimean War brought Elswick into contact with the War Office, perhaps for the first time. Armstrong was asked to design some underwater mines to blow up the Russian ships which had been sunk in the entrance to Sebastopol harbour. He set to work in his usual conscientious fashion. Within a few weeks he had produced a device consisting of a wrought-iron cylinder loaded with gun-cotton. A number of experiments were carried out and Armstrong invited his principal employees to observe a trial in his fields at Jesmond. 'It was a very pleasant function and greatly enjoyed by all the guests. The mines, planted in different parts of the field, exploded in the most exhilarating manner, and after tea had been served out, the party separated delighted with the afternoon's entertainment.'

Armstrong's invention was never in fact used. But this first contact with the War Office was to have a fundamental influence both on Armstrong and on the development of armaments in this country. A revolution was about to begin with Armstrong at its head. As a result he was to become one of the greatest industrialists in the world, and Tyneside was to become one of the greatest industrial centres.

# CHAPTER THREE

## THE CRIMEAN WAR

FEW events of such apparent insignificance can have had greater repercussions than the Crimean War. Fought in an unknown penninsula, for a cause that has always seemed obscure and using military techniques that were backward and almost barbarian, it led to many changes: in diplomatic relations, in military science, in nursing and even in the education of women. Fifty years before, Russia and Great Britain had fought side by side against France. Now Britain and France were allies against Russia's attempted encroachment into the Balkans. But the war exposed the incompetence of the British higher command, the lack of organization and staff work, the totally out-dated ability of the guns, and the alarming absence of proper medical provision. The British lost 19,600 lives—15,700 of them by disease, many of them in the hospital wards of Scutari. According to G. M. Trevelyan: 'The real hero of the war was Florence Nightingale and its most indubitable outcome was modern nursing, both military and civil, and a new conception of the potentiality and place in society of the trained and educated woman. And this in turn led, in the 'sixties and 'seventies, to John Stuart Mill's movement for women's suffrage, which Miss Nightingale supported, and to the founding of women's colleges and the improvement of girls' schools, when at length some provision was made for the neglected higher education of one half of the Queen's subjects.'[1]

The war also had a profound effect upon William Armstrong's career and no event more than the battle of Inkerman. This was fought on 5th November 1854, a day of swirling fog. In fact, many commentators say it was only the fog that saved the British from being overwhelmed by much bigger Russian forces; that, and the belated use of two 18-pound smooth-bore guns, each weighing over two tons. Late in the battle the guns were hauled up from a seige train and trundled into the middle of the English line on the heights of Inkerman. From there, they had a devastating effect on the enemy batteries at Shell Hill and eventually forced their withdrawal. But getting the two 18-pounders up the Inkerman heights was a stupendous task. For some reason, no draught horses were available. The guns had to be manhandled. Although the distance was only one and a half miles, the country was rough and there was a deep ravine in the way. The team of 150 men struggled for three hours to get the guns into position. During that time hundreds of lives were lost.

By the end of the day, the British dead numbered 632, with 1,873 wounded, while the French casualties were 1,726 killed or wounded. One historian wrote: 'All over the battlefield men could be found in every possible contorted attitude, sometimes in couples who, with bayonet in hand, had simultaneously transfixed each other. Even a year later they were still being discovered in the thick brushwood or in the rock crannies, either having been killed outright or having crawled into some rude shelter, there to die in agony.'[2]

The public, reading of these events at home, was appalled. Sixty years later Lord Rendel remembered the scene when his father and William Armstrong, who was staying with him, read of the news. 'I remember well my father's animated outburst at the absurd ponderousness of the cannon so critically employed. My father had been the first engineer to construct, at the age of twenty-three, a continuous iron-bridge over an estuary of the sea near Plymouth. That bridge was, of course, of cast-iron. Thirty years had passed since that bridge was built and the use of cast-iron for such a purpose had become utterly antiquated. My father was indignant that military engineering should have lagged so far behind civil engineering as to be still retaining cast-iron for the purpose of making cannon, of which the very earliest examples, over 200 years old, had been constructed in wrought-iron. He dwelt upon the apathy and backwardness exhibited by the military engineers in not seeking to give to field artillery the advantages of rifling already attained in the small arms ...

'On this eventful morning I remember my father pointing to the great lightness and strength of the small-arm barrel

constructed of wrought-iron which rendered the use of cylin-
drical bullets and rifling possible. He asked why the extraordinary advance, secured for small arms by civilians in the
interests mainly of sport, had not been extended by the military authorities to field artillery and even heavy artillery.

'I can see my father and Lord Armstrong now before me
with a bit of blotting paper between them on the table, on
which Lord Armstrong drew out a scheme for an enlargement
to field-gun size of the small-arm wrought-iron rifle; and I
can almost hear my father's challenge to Lord Armstrong to
take up the question and bring artillery up to the level of the
civil engineering science of the day. "You are the man to do
it." '³

Clearly someone had to. Guns, of one kind or another, had
been in existence since the fourteenth century. But developments had been very slow. A cast-iron type of production had
been adopted in the mid-sixteenth century but since then few
changes had been made. The gun remained unaltered as a
closed-ended tube formed from a solid piece of metal.

There had been some small refinements over the years.
Better methods of casting or boring had been developed but
in essence the field gun of the 1840's was only a slightly more
sophisticated version of a gun that soldiers of the sixteenth or
seventeenth century would have recognized. This is not to
say that research work had not been carried out. It had. But
the apparently insuperable problem posed by the choice of
metal had not been overcome. Armourers still remained
dreadfully ignorant of the scientific principles involved in
artillery—and sometimes paid for their ignorance with their
lives. In particular, cast-iron guns were very unreliable. They
were always blowing up. In fact, they were often more dangerous to their users than to the enemy. Yet this method of
manufacture had remained in use long after better methods
had become available in other branches of engineering. But
now at last, under the stimulus of the Crimean War, change
was on the way. Within the next thirty years a complete
revolution was to take place, transforming armaments from a
basically sixteenth-century concept to one we would appreciate today. No one played a more important part than
Armstrong.

He and James Rendel continued to turn their ideas over in their minds. A month later, in December 1854, they wrote to Sir James Graham 'suggesting the expediency', in Armstrong's own words, 'of enlarging the ordinary rifle to the standard of a field gun and using elongated projectiles of lead instead of balls of cast-iron. This communication was handed by Sir James Graham to the Duke of Newcastle, then Minister for War, with whom I had an interview on the subject, in company with Mr Rendel. At this interview I was authorized by his Grace to carry my views into effect, by constructing upon the plan I had suggested one or more guns, not exceeding six in number, and to make the necessary experiments in connection with the subject.'[4]

## ARMSTRONG'S FIRST GUN

As a simple design, Armstrong's idea was not particularly new or exciting. Everyone involved in armament making had been saying for many years that 'elongated projectiles' should supersede 'balls of cast-iron'. Everyone was also agreed that rifling should produce a far higher standard of accuracy. No one, however, had yet solved the metallurgical and mechanical problems involved in improving accuracy and reliability while reducing weight. With the Duke of Newcastle's backing, this is what Armstrong now set out to do, as others had before him and indeed others were doing at the same time as him.

Lord Rendel, one of the three sons of James Rendel, recalled in his memoirs: 'So far from attempting to produce the six guns ordered, Lord Armstrong was in no hurry to produce one. He was resolute to reserve the revelation until he could show that he had solved certain serious difficulties. The first difficulty was that of a safe and easily worked breech mechanism. The second was that of absorbing the far greater recoil of the much-lightened piece without injury to the carriage. The third was the overcoming of the difficulty of providing a self-igniting shell and shrapnel. It was the third problem that consumed the most time and gave the most trouble.'[5]

Armstrong himself wrote: 'The substitution of elongated solid projectiles for spherical bullets is an essential step to the attainment of very extended range in artillery practice; but the lengthening of a solid projectile involves the necessity of strengthening the gun to enable it to resist the greater intensity of force which becomes necessary to give the required velocity; and this object can only be effected, consistently with lightness, by constructing the gun of steel or wrought-iron, instead of cast-iron or bronze.'

He began by considering the question of the correct metal to use and he carried out some tests to discover the relative tensile strengths. Cast-steel offered the greatest strength and cast-iron the least. But cast-steel could not be used because 'in the present state of manufacture, to produce it in masses sufficiently large without the occurrence of flaws which, in the great majority of cases would destroy its efficiency' was impossible. Sheer steel or wrought-iron held out better possibilities. Armstrong conducted some tests with these materials forged to the correct dimensions and then bored in the usual manner. Unfortunately this method of manufacture exposed only too clearly 'great uncertainty in the strength of the material, and rendered it impossible to define the thickness necessary to resist a given charge of powder. I felt compelled, therefore, to dismiss this mode of construction and to adopt another more correct in principle, but more difficult of execution.' Instead of forging the gun out of a single piece of metal, he would build up its thickness.

In his experiments, Armstrong had found that steel was more difficult to weld than iron because more defects seemed to show up. But he appreciated that it was a harder substance and a better choice for the surface of the bore. He decided to use steel as an inner lining 'and to obtain the necessary strength by encircling it with twisted cylinders of wrought-iron, tightly contracted upon the steel core by the usual process of cooling after previous expansion by heat.' In other words, he built up the required thickness by shrinking an outer cylinder upon an inner one. 'Considerable difficulties were encountered in carrying this plan into practice but I ultimately succeeded in completing a gun.' The most difficult part was rifling. This was done by Mr William Bradley, one of the leading foremen, during nightshift watched by Armstrong, who was unable to sleep.

The next problem was breech loading. Armstrong decided

that the best solution was to close the bore by a block or vent piece which would drop into a slot in the breech and would be fixed by tightening a large screw. This system was not particularly suitable and gave a lot of trouble. In fact the vent piece sometimes blew out, putting the gun out of action as well as endangering life, including Armstrong's own. Alfred Cochrane, in his reminiscences, declared: 'All this time Mr Armstrong had been investigating problems entirely new to him with his usual thoroughness and enthusiasm. He fired his gun across the dene at Jesmond against the opposite hillside and the numerous adventures which he met with during these firing trials, as well as the narrow escapes he had of blowing himself to pieces, were most exciting. In those days there was no science of artillery such as there is today—nor was there any knowledge of what pressure metals would stand, and our illustrious founder deserves some credit for his physical courage in wrestling with this unknown and perilous subject.'[6]

The final problem was the projectile. Armstrong wrote: 'The resistance which a projectile encounters in passing through the air is mainly dependent upon the area of its cross-section, and the advantage of lengthening a bullet consists in augmenting the weight without increasing this sectional area; but in order to realise this advantage, it is essential that the bullet be guided endways in its course, and this can only be effected by causing it to rotate rapidly upon its longer axis, which is accomplished by firing it from a rifled bore.'

Armstrong found out many useful properties of projectiles as a result of his many experiments. He found how to improve accuracy and how to increase the range, he found the right shape to use for the bullet or shell and the right mixture for the gunpowder.

His research led him to produce projectiles made of cast-iron, thinly coated with lead. The lead was crushed in the barrel's grooves giving rotation but preventing the huge recoil that was common at the time with conventional guns. The fuse in the shell was also cleverly thought out so that it could be set to explode immediately upon leaving the muzzle, like grapeshot, or only when it hit the target, thus having a powerful concentrated impact. Armstrong said: 'The percussion arrangement is such that the shell, while in the hands of a friend, is so safe and quiescent that it may be thrown off the top of a house without exploding but among enemies it is so sensitive and mischievous that the slightest touch will cause it to explode.' The act of firing the shell changed the fuse from half to full cock, as it were.

In the end, he produced a gun with a greater range than the gun then employed by the Services, with a greater accuracy and with a substantial reduction in weight. His first gun weighed five hundredweights. The guns that were lugged up Inkerman Heights weighed 42 hundredweights each.

As was usual with him, Armstrong concentrated all his energies upon the task in hand. One account noted: 'Experimental guns were built and trials made at all kinds of unseasonable hours and out-of-the-way places, on the moors of Allenheads, among the lead mines and sheep farms and by the sea-shore. While pursuing these tests, it is well-known that the inhabitants of many a rustic home were disturbed by the alarming sounds of cannon now and again reverberating through the Northumbrian hills. Many strange rumours were brought to Newcastle about the French having invaded the country and marched up into the wilds of Durham at night-time.'[7]

One of the workmen who took part in the early attempts to produce a gun recalled: 'The first indication we had ... was seeing a bar of steel being forged under sledge-hammers (for there were no steam hammers at that time). This was the first gun barrel. Then came the drilling, which was slow work, as the steel was hard. When at last a hole was bored through it was found to be very crooked and was very difficult to straighten. It was not without much trouble, spreading over months, that all the other operations were completed, as many of them were done with makeshift tools.'

This anonymous workman also gave a fascinating glimpse of the works. 'At this time the traffic was worked with one horse and cart. The heavy traffic, as at present, was conveyed up the incline by rail, but with this difference, that there was no hauling engine at the top or friendly locomotive at the bottom to give a push. You will wonder how we managed. Well, when a truck was ready, the word was passed through the shops and every man and boy turned out and we pulled the truck up with long drag ropes. This was a jolly time in fine weather and after a pull up the bank it took us some time to settle down to work again.'

Armstrong delivered the first gun, which cost £1,000 to make, to the War Office in July 1855, just seven months after his first interview with the Duke of Newcastle. The trials went very well but the Ordnance Committee felt the gun was too small to be of any practical importance. They sent it back to Elswick and asked for it to be re-bored to take a normal five-pound shot instead of the original three-pound shot. Armstrong obliged. By December 1856 he was ready to submit his new design to the War Office. It proved successful and, according to a U.S. observer, 'good practice was obtained at 1,500 and 2,000 yards'.


BIGGER GUNS

The following year, Armstrong was ready with a bigger version, capable of firing 18-pound shells. This was tested both at Newcastle and at the Army's official range centre at Shoeburyness.

For comparison, it was put up against smooth-bore guns of similar calibre. It was found that 'the rifled gun could make better practice at a distance of two miles than the smooth bore could at one mile'. Two more 18-pounders and a 12-pounder were ordered. The diehards in the Services were convinced or, if not convinced, they at least agreed that the new system of artillery should be accepted under Service conditions for further, more detailed and more extensive testing.

After a long and difficult time, it looked as if all Armstrong's research effort was to be vindicated. He had worked tirelessly on this project, concentrating upon it to the virtual exclusion of everything else. It was of course a big risk to take, both financially and in terms of the neglect of the rest of the business. But this was his way. He had exhibited exactly the same dedication in the past on other projects. As he himself said : 'I attribute my success to always keeping a definite aim before me and devoting my whole energies towards its attainment.' He had not taken a holiday since setting up as a manufacturer eleven years previously. It was to be another four years yet before he could feel safe to take one. 'I have had my full share of difficulties' he recalled and while the difficulties remained he could not put them out of his mind to slip off for a holiday.

While it was agreed that a new system of artillery should be adopted, there was no agreement about whose system should be adopted, for numerous inventors were at work. Clearly Armstrong was one of the main aspirants. But there were others, particularly Joseph Whitworth of Manchester. And they were all determined to win Government favour.

So specific did the arguments and the rival claims become that the Government decided to set up a Committee on Rifled Cannon and it began its work in August 1858. By this time Armstrong had manufactured about half a dozen guns. He could show therefore that he was not only capable of designing guns but also of making them. He had developed a new technique of coiled rifling, a new kind of projectile and a new breech. In contrast, Whitworth was able to show the committee only his new design, which incorporated the concept of polygonal rifling. He had not manufactured from scratch a gun with these design features. In fact, he had not been wholly responsible for manufacturing any gun at his headquarters in Manchester. What he had done was to rifle guns supplied to him by the Government. It was one of these guns, made of brass, that Whitworth used to compete against Armstrong at the official trials.

The investigations, although short, were thorough. At the end of their deliberations in November 1859, the Committee had no hesitation in recommending the Armstrong gun.

The summing up in the report said: 'The range and precision of the gun are so vastly superior to all field ordnance at this time that after careful and repeated tests, the committee appointed to investigate the question recommends the adoption of the gun as the Field Gun of the Service.' In coming to that conclusion, the Committee reported: 'Your Committee have had no practical evidence before them that even at this moment any other method of constructing rifled ordnance exists which can be compared with that of Mr Armstrong.'

The Secretary of State for War told the House of Commons:

'The accuracy ... at 3,000 yards was as seven to one compared with that of the common gun at 1,000 yards; while at 1,000 yards it would hit an object every time which was struck by the common guns only once in fifty-seven times; therefore, at equal distances, the Armstrong gun was fifty-seven times as accurate as our common artillery.'[7] The Commander-in-Chief of the British Army, the Duke of Cambridge, added his tribute. 'The gun,' he said, 'could do everything but speak.'[8]

## THE TRIUMPH

Armstrong had reached the high point of his career. Now aged 49, the engineer who had given up the law only twelve years previously became a national hero. He had, of course, already made a considerable name for himself in engineering and scientific circles. Now his name was to be known to everyone. For a country's existence depended on its security, as the politicians continually told the people. Here was the new supplier of that security, the inventor and manufacturer of a system of artillery more deadly, more mobile than anything then known.

One historian wrote: 'Looking back upon the position, we can hardly imagine that any inventor has ever occupied so commanding a place as did Mr Armstrong at this moment. His previous discoveries and researches had brought him wealth and fame but his guns must have opened up to him visions of untold riches and influence. European nations were trying to outbid each other for the possession of the new artillery and here was the one man who had the coveted secrets and the necessary knowledge. About a year earlier there had been laid down at Elswick a plant for the manufacture of the guns and their accessories, and the Elswick workmen, noted for their mechanical skill, had acquired experience of the treatment of the material, so that the making of the ordnance had already begun and there was nothing to hinder guns being supplied to anybody who would buy them.

'When the English Government decided to adopt the Armstrong system, it was open to the inventor of that system to make his own terms with them. He held the patents and he might have maintained a monopoly by introducing and patenting new improvements or he might have cultivated a very profitable connection with foreign countries.

'The course which Mr Armstrong took was at once the most public-spirited and the most generous. He made a gift of his patents to the nation, and, what was of even greater value, he entered the Government service as Engineer to the War Department ... In recognition of his services to the State, the great engineer received a knighthood.'⁹ He was made a Commander of the Order of the Bath and given £2,000 a year salary, back-dated to 1856.

The *Northern Weekly Standard* carried a comment under the title 'The Strong Arm'. It began: 'All honour to the Armstrong that has given us the Strong Arm.' Then it advocated the speedy introduction of Armstrong artillery for the defence of the nation. 'Decorations are all very well. But the order to which a meritorious engineer aspires is not the Order of the Garter or the Order of the Thistle or the Order of St Patrick or of the Bath but an order for more cannon.'

His appointment was announced on 22nd February 1859. A week later, he visited Elswick for the first time since the news was announced. A contemporary report stated: 'Great preparations were made to give him a cordial reception. The shops and offices were decorated with flags and streamers; the workmen and their wives and families came out in holiday attire; and a row of cannon was planted on an elevation facing the river. Sir William arrived at the gates of the factory in his carriage at three o'clock and was saluted with loud and prolonged acclamations. A highly congratulatory address was read by Mr Hutchinson, the Works Manager, to which Sir William suitably responded.'

An indication of the extent of Hutchinson's congratulations can be gained from but one typical sentence: 'We, who have been occasionally permitted to witness your indomitable perseverance in pursuing your experiments under the most perplexing circumstances with the most extraordinary zeal and energy, and have observed how frequently your disappointments and failures have been made the key to successful attainments of your purposes, have become involuntarily interested in your triumphant success and do most sincerely rejoice that to some extent the value of your invention and services are recognized by the government of your country.'

A great celebration began, during which one of the work-men, not to be outdone by Hutchinson, sang a song he had composed entitled 'The Armstrong Gun', the words of which were as follows:

The Armstrong Gun, the Armstrong Gun,
What a wonderful thing is the Armstrong Gun,
Sir William's invention astonisht them all,
Wi' a bolt for a shot instead of a ball.

Nae spungin' or ramin' or servin' the vent—
Such things are no' needed to serve its intent.
In a neat little chamber breech end of the bore
Place the powder and shot and away let it roar.

Then ther's fuses, they're said, such wonders I tell,
They 'splode the bolt shells when it pleases themsel's
It's short range or long range, it's a' the same thing,
Jest set 'em—they're true to the secret spring.

The gunboats hae now lost their glory and pride,
For wor gun sends its bolts slapbang thro' its side,
Neither iron or oak can resist its ava,
When it vomits them forth frae its terrible jaws.

So success to Sir William, and long may it thrive!
May his days be as glad as the bees in his hive,
Wi' his greatness of mind, he's the patience of Job,
He's now made a gun that can conquer the Globe!

This was only the beginning of a grand series of celebrations. On Tuesday, 10th May 1859, Armstrong and his wife were guests of honour at a 'splendid banquet' in the Assembly Rooms. It was a night for the most fulsome and, to our minds, the most embarrassing compliments. The toasts to Armstrong lasted over three hours. The chairman for the evening, Sir George Grey, M.P., declared: 'Let me, as a Northumbrian, express my sincere sympathy with those feelings which I know animate the minds of the numerous friends of Sir

William Armstrong, whom I see around me, that his name has been added to the roll of other great men, whose genius and whose successful cultivation of that genius, whose energy and whose high character, have shed a lustre upon that part of the kingdom with which we are immediately connected and whose fame, travelling far beyond the limits of that neighbourhood, still proud to call him its son, has filled not only our own country, but has pervaded Europe, and has extended to the utmost limits of the civilized world.' He then started to enumerate the achievements. Turning eventually to Armstrong's invention of rifled cannon, Sir George said: 'If the occasion should arise—if England should be forced to engage in a necessary and defensive war—if that occasion should arise, England will not be found deficient with such a gun; and I say we may confidently anticipate that while we have among us men of the genius, of the perseverance, of the energy, of the liberality and of the patriotism of Sir William Armstrong, this country will be found behind no other country in the world in the efficiency of its armaments and in the means of conducting such a war to a successful and triumphant issue.'

Rolling sentences tumbled out of Sir George for more than an hour. At last, it was Armstrong's turn to reply. 'Coming, as this compliment does, from the inhabitants of a locality in which I was born, and in which I have spent nearly my whole life, I look upon it as a mark of personal kindness rather than of public approbation and as such I will remember it with pride and gratitude as long as I live,' he said.

## THE MORAL DILEMMA

The eulogies from a worshipping public and the long, pains-taking research and development work itself tended to sidestep one central and crucial aspect about Armstrong's new work. What he was doing, what he had invested so much time and money in achieving and what the public was now applauding was a more efficient means of killing people. The armament manufacturer stands in a uniquely isolated position. When employed, his products have the sole purpose of death. Other products, of course, may result in death. None, but armaments are expressly designed for the purpose.

How did Armstrong view the moral dilemma? Although he gave it thought, there is no evidence that he agonized over the decision to go into armament manufacture. Only occasionally did he feel the need to defend himself. 'If I thought that war would be fomented, or the interests of humanity suffer, by what I have done, I would greatly regret it. I have no such apprehension.' Indeed he thought his work might actually decrease bloodshed. He developed this particular argument in two ways. In the first, he argued that armaments, or security which was what they represented, were part of civilization. 'The power which science gives us,' he said, 'whether as applied to peace or war, is always on the side of civilization and the spread of civilization must tend necessarily to diminish war and to make it less barbarous.'[10]

As a statement that begs many questions. If science gives the power for greater warfare can that really be 'on the side of civilization'? Could civilization be consistent with the production of armaments as a well-organized and respected industry? Whatever the answer to such philosophical questions, clearly Armstrong exhibited an ignorance of historical experience. The Greek and Roman civilizations, for example, had shown a penchant for war. So had civilized Europe. The Crimean War, which had just ended, had been fought by three 'civilized' nations. Indeed, if anything, it was a religious war —by Armstrong's standards, a contradiction. There has never been any evidence that 'the spread of civilization must tend necessarily to diminish war'.

The other way in which he developed the argument has a very modern ring to it. 'It is our province, as engineers,' he said on another occasion, 'to make the forces of matter obedient to the will of man; and those who use the means we supply must be responsible for their legitimate application.' An argument that the nuclear scientists of today would recognize instantly.

Armstrong used other arguments too from time to time. He said: 'We, as a nation, have few men to spare for war and we have need of all the aid that science can give us to secure us against aggression and to enable us to hold in subjection the vast and semi-barbarous population which we have to rule in the East.'

His audience murmured their approval. Of course he was uttering the conventional wisdom of the day. Britain had a duty in the East. The 'semi-barbarous population' was being enriched by its subjection to Britain and since that subjection depended on military might, it was possible to argue that armament manufacture was actually helping civilization to advance.

On another occasion, he declared: 'When battles were fought hand to hand, war, so far as mechanics are concerned, was an affair of muscular force, and was in that form the most sanguinary, because combats were the most close. When other forces were called into play, inventive appliances became necessary, and these as they have advanced have more and more widened the distances separating combatants and have thus operated to prevent that greater sacrifice to life which would otherwise have resulted from the employment of more destructive weapons. It is therefore not to be supposed that future wars will be rendered more murderous by the intervention of the engineer. On the contrary, we may fairly anticipate that, the more the element of intelligence supersedes that of animal force in military struggles, the more will the barbarity of war be mitigated.'[12]

What a cruelly forlorn prophecy in the light of the First World War when the millions who died or suffered probably represented a higher number than in all the world's other wars put together.

His colleagues and rivals in the armament business used arguments similar to Armstrong's. Joseph Whitworth said: 'The greater the precision with which firearms may be used at long distances and the more their powers of destruction are increased, the more reluctant will civilized nations be to use them against each other.'

However, not everyone agreed. Even some of Armstrong's own employees were against the move into arms. Richard Hoskin, one of the company's earliest and best craftsmen, a Cornishman and a Quaker, felt unable to help in drawing up plans for the first gun.

'Thou knowest, Mr Armstrong, that I cannot go against my conscience,' he said during the course of a long discussion with his employer. The latter finally declared that he could not blame Hoskin for his loyal adherence to his principles. Armstrong himself suffered from no moral doubts. The problems for him were scientific and industrial. The most pressing now was manufacturing capacity.

And the *Newcastle Daily Chronicle* of 27th December 1900 said on his death: 'Lord Armstrong may be best remembered in the end, by the world at large, as a strangely representative figure of the latest phase of nineteenth-century civilization. On the one hand, we have the most wonderful machinery of production that has ever been known; on the other, we have the most tremendous machinery of murder. We subject the rudest powers of nature to the services of peace and we employ the most refined powers of the intellect to devise methods of destruction more awful than flood or earthquake. It is a situation that could hardly have been anticipated half a century ago whether by the most extravagant hope or the most fantastic apprehension ... There is something that appals the imagination in the application of a cool and temperate mind like Lord Armstrong's to the science of destruction. We do not know whether all this is such a monstrous paradox as it seems. Nothing could have been more unexpected by the earlier prophets of democracy than the apparent return of militarism with a vengeance at the end of the liberal and humanitarian century. They thought war and the crime of kings and peace the protege of peoples. They thought that free trade and low franchise would make armies obsolete and put the diplomatist out of date. If a bygone generation of reformers could revisit the earth they would have a disheartening sense that there had been a miscalculation somewhere. And yet there may have been a miscalculation of methods only and not of results.

The world if never so equipped for war was never so reluctant to make it. The sight of means to do ill-deeds all round keeps the ill-deeds undone. In the nature of things the militarism of the time must bring its own abatement and Elswick in the end may prove a more effective advocate of peace than Exeter Hall.'

So, in the end, the moral dilemma pointed out so clearly in this obituary, was shrugged off. The terrible irony of those false hopes does not need emphasizing. The awful prospect did not deter men from killing one another in huge numbers and arms manufacturers, like Armstrong, must be held responsible for supplying the means. But mankind itself must take the ultimate blame for wanting to use those means and for making the position of the arms manufacturer such a respectable, indeed glorified role.

A very big increase in armament manufacture was needed. But the arsenal at Woolwich, ill-equipped and inefficiently run, could not cope. The obvious alternative was Elswick. Here were the men who had done the original development work. There was room for expansion. Elswick it was.

At the same time there was a feeling that it would not be right for Armstrong to have a financial interest and that a separate company should be formed. What authority this feeling had is not clear. Certainly Armstrong himself declared in 1859: 'Of course I never dreamt of giving up my present business; on the contrary it was distinctly stipulated that I should remain at liberty to carry on any business that I chose. This stipulation may or may not be in accordance with pre-cedent but I trust that the public will feel assured, from the general course I have followed in this matter, that personal aggrandisement is not the course I have in view.'[12]

Clearly he would not have made such a remark if personal comments were not being made about him. After all, the Government had given him a top job at £2,000 a year to be payable as from 1856-1865. They had agreed to pay all his research and development costs since 1855. And they had thrown in a knighthood and a C.B. Of course, he had given his patents to the nation but there were those who were be-ginning to say he was being well rewarded. It was probably to head off such criticism that his friends advocated the forma-tion of a new company without any financial involvement by himself.

THE ELSWICK ORDNANCE COMPANY

In any case, that is what happened. The Elswick Ordnance Company was created. The partners were Mr Cruddas, Mr Lambert and Mr George Rendel. He was one of three Rendel brothers who at one time or another were associated with the firm. Their father, James, was of course the close friend of Armstrong's who had played a decisive part at two stages in his career, first pushing him from the law into engineering by promising to place orders for his hydraulic cranes; and then, by encouraging him to consider the problems of artillery. Now, just as Armstrong had been taken under the wing of Armorer Donkin, George Rendel who was still in his twenties was taken under Armstrong's wing. For three years he lived in the Armstrong house in Jesmond Dene. And now he was made one of the three partners of this throbbing new enterprise as well as being appointed the general manager.

His brother, later Lord Rendel, wrote: 'My brother George was then about twenty-five or twenty-six years of age. He had been Lord Armstrong's constant companion during the experiments with the first gun. He had shared to the full the enthusiasm for the prospective development of artillery manufacture and he had been mainly concerned in the providing of plant for the construction of guns.'[13]

The capital of £50,000 was guaranteed by the Government. It also promised full and constant employment in return for the firm's guarantee to supply no other government but itself. A formal agreement was drawn up between General Peel, the Secretary of State for War, and the three partners. To cope with the increase in business, some more land was bought at Elswick to the east of the existing premises and some new buildings were erected. A large amount of new machinery was also ordered.

It was about this time too that Armstrong made one of his shrewdest appointments. One of his greatest qualities in fact was the ability to choose the right man for senior appointments. This was true of George Cruddas who had handled the company's financial affairs with great acumen since the beginning. It was true of George Hutchinson the Works Manager and of George Rendel, the youthful but gifted manager of the Ordnance Works. And it was now to be particularly true of a young Artillery officer called Andrew Noble, then aged 29. He had been secretary to the Special Committee on Rifled Cannon that had sat in 1858 and to the Committee on Plates and Guns that sat the following year. But it was not these

committees so much as the Ordnance Select Committee of
1860 that brought Armstrong into close contact with Noble.
He liked the look of the young officer and he certainly admired
his technical knowledge and his commanding personality.

Armstrong offered Noble a place with the new Ordnance
Company. At first Noble demurred. But then he decided to
give Elswick a try. He obtained leave to join the company for
a few months. After seeing the possibilities at first hand, his
mind was made up. He joined the company in 1860 as joint
manager of the Ordnance Works with Rendel. The following
year he was admitted into partnership and eventually he was
to go on to become Armstrong's successor, in full control of
the whole works.

Armstrong's success was now enormous. He was a national
hero, a top Government adviser, a large-scale manufacturer
of a wide range of products and clearly he was now going
to become much more important still. But, above all, he
represented what the Victorians loved—a self-made man. Of
course, his father had acquired some money and William had
been properly brought up and nicely educated. That was not
quite the point. As far as his present success was concerned,
he had achieved it himself, from nothing. He had taken a
quite ridiculous risk. But it had come off. And now here he
was just twelve years later thoroughly vindicated, a figure of
national reputation and a perfect example for every father
to set before his sons of where application and determination
could lead. And if any of those lectured-to little boys protested that Armstrong had gone against his father's wishes
in going into industry, well that would be brushed aside with
a smile or a grimace, as mood or personality dictated.

THE BANK CRASH

Of course, even someone as overwhelmingly successful as
Armstrong found that difficulties still tended to crop up. For
example, there was the problem caused by the crash of the
company's bankers. From the first, W. G. Armstrong and
Company had banked with the Northumberland and Durham
District Bank, the strongest in the North at the time. But
even though it was the strongest, it was unable to withstand

a strong wave of withdrawals in November 1857. It was forced to close its doors for ever. The disaster occurred rapidly.

In the spring of 1857, just six months earlier, the directors had reported that the previous year's business had 'fully answered the expectations of the directors and affords a very satisfactory result'.

From that moment, however, business went into reverse. A large Newcastle firm collapsed, owing the bank a substantial sum of money. Suspicions began to grow in the minds of deposit holders. Throughout the summer they gradually withdrew their money. Then on November 22nd a rumour started in London that the Bank was in 'embarrassed circumstances'. Five days later the Bank posted the following announcement on its doors: 'The Directors ... lament to announce that owing to a long continued monetary pressure and the difficulty of rendering available the resources of the Bank, they have felt themselves obliged to suspend its operations. Deposits and Credit Balances will be fully paid with as little delay as possible.'

The following day the Bank of England in Grey Street was besieged by anxious employers who wanted to borrow money for the week's wages bill. They feared riots among the men if the money was not forthcoming. Fortunately, Armstrong's balance at the Northumberland and Durham District Bank was not very substantial at that moment. The company was able to view the situation with a degree of equanimity. Even so, it decided the following week, 2nd December, to transfer its account to the Bank of England.

The financial crisis was quickly solved. But the falling orders for cranes, the original product, was worrying. Since 1855 when a high point had been reached, crane manufacture had been going into reverse. It was a new trend. Since the inception in 1847 the sales graph had been triumphantly upwards. By mid-1850's ninety cranes a year were being built. Now the figures were falling right back to less than fifty a year. It was very disappointing and there did not seem any reason for it. There were no wars on at the time which might affect businessmen's investment habits. Nor was there a lull in the general economy. The other obvious alternative was probably the true cause—the new product had found its initial market. It now had to await evaluation. After that sales would pick up again. Indeed this is what happened. In the early 1860's sales began to shoot up to an all-time peak of over 150 a year—as the reputation of the cranes, now fully tested in working conditions, began to spread.

If these problems caused Armstrong some small anxiety, there were of course now plenty of triumphs. In 1860 he was elected the sixth President of the Newcastle Literary and Philosophical Society, which he had joined in 1836. He was by far its most distinguished member. He had also been a very active member, certainly before he became a manufacturer. He had done his share of lecturing too. In 1844 he had given two lectures on hydro-electricity to the Society's members. The following year he had lectured three times on the use of water for motive power.

As he grew busier, he could not afford the same amount of time for the Society but he continued to support it wholeheartedly in other ways. In 1858 he gave the Society 1,300 of his father's books. The Society's official historian commented that it 'obtained a more complete Mathematical Department than any other provincial institution in the kingdom'. The following year Armstrong put up £1,450 to pay the full cost of a new lecture room. He was to remain an ever-ready benefactor. In 1885 he gave the Society £700 while all the other members together provided £750 towards the cost of a new wing to the premises. In his later years, once he had retired from active interest in the works, he gave some more lectures: one on a visit to Egypt; another on some electrical experiments.

He was also to become President of the British Association for the Advancement of Science, as we shall see. And he was in great demand everywhere as a speaker on this subject or a lecturer in that. But while he enjoyed his triumph, his success was soon to be called into question. For while he was entering the peak of his career, he was also entering a period of personal and professional controversy, a controversy so bitter and prolonged that eventually he had to relinquish his new official position.

# CHAPTER FOUR

## THE STORM BREAKS

ARMSTRONG'S triumph was never absolute. These years of greatest success were marked equally by controversy, criticism and even revenge. His opponents in armament manufacture were not prepared to accept defeat gracefully. They put forward their claims with great vigour and tried to demolish his with ferocity. They called for independent trials. When they proved unsatisfactory from their point of view, they called for a Government enquiry. When that proved equally unfruitful, they called for other enquiries, longer and more detailed. They got their friends to write letters to newspapers, to publish articles in newspapers, even to go so far as to publish a 350-page book expertly denigrating Armstrong's work and advancing theirs.

One can imagine the impact of a sustained campaign of this kind on Armstrong. A close friend of his wrote: 'Lord Armstrong found he was being exposed to publicity in a form peculiarly obnoxious to his reserved and reticent character. He suffered acutely under the sting of heated and personal controversy.' All his powers of tenacity and dedication were called upon, not to solve a scientific problem in the quietness of his laboratory, a situation he knew well, but to defend himself and his inventions against bitter opponents in the noisy, ruffled sphere of public debate. His rivals, especially Whitworth, were not only vindictive, they were indefatigable. They believed his products were inferior to theirs and they were ready to say so at any time and all the time.

Unfortunately, these manufacturing rivals were not the only ones Armstrong faced. He had also to meet the more insidious, Establishment arguments of the Service officers of the day. Their conservatism was notorious. But being insiders, they could spread their arguments in the right direction without Armstrong even knowing who was saying what or to whom. In such a closed world, rumours could catch alight and travel like wild-fire. His guns would not work—they were dangerous. Or alternatively, if they would work, they could not be serviced and maintained very easily. Or alternatively, if they could, they would lead to too many changes. The soldiers would not accept them. The officers would not accept them. Why not leave well alone? Go back to the tried methods, the methods that had served well, the methods that after all had beaten the French fifty years before.

Then there was something else too—the price of the Armstrong guns. Was it really necessary for the Government to pay so much for these Elswick weapons? Would not it be much cheaper to manufacture them at Woolwich? Armstrong had given the patents to the nation. There could be no secret expertise. The skilled craftsmen at the Government arsenal could soon pick up what the men of Elswick, who had no tradition of armament manufacture, had learnt so quickly.

Each of these three lines of attack would have been difficult to repulse. Combined, they were irresistible. Armstrong found himself and his work coming under fire virtually every week, sometimes every day. He had to defend himself before seven searching Government enquiries within five years. It was an extremely wearying and disheartening period, which offset to a large measure any feeling of personal satisfaction that he might have had at his success or his elevated position.

The dispute first broke out in that celebrated 'ring' for opponents, the letters column of The Times. A Captain E. P. Halsted was particularly incisive in his comments. But it spread to other publications, too. The Mechanics Magazine, for example, carried a number of articles, apparently of a 'fair and impartial' character. It carried reports from Major R. J. Hay, the assistant Adjutant General to the Royal Artillery Expeditionary Force in China, supposedly claiming that the Armstrong gun had caused accidents among British troops and had had to be withdrawn at the critical moment. The magazine also stated that the average price of the Armstrong guns was £2,000.

These statements were simply untrue and it is difficult even now to understand why Armstrong's opponents should have become so wild in their accusations. Armstrong had no

difficulty in refuting the quoted comments from Major Hay
—indeed Hay did it for him.

In a letter to Armstrong he complained bitterly of the way
he had been completely misreported by the scientific and daily
press. His view of the guns was entirely the opposite to his
reportedly critical views. 'The Armstrong Guns in China
rendered the most valuable service, being always in the most
efficient and serviceable condition, although put to very
severe tests. They were never withdrawn from action and
their places supplied by others; on the contrary, the Armstrong guns were invariably the first to be ordered up when
artillery was required.'[1] Major Hay admitted that of course
there were small defects, but nothing like so serious as the
exaggerated press comments had suggested. He gave his summing up as: 'I now feel confident that the British artillery
have the first gun with the most perfect ammunition in the
world.'

There were other supporters. Baring, the Under-Secretary
for War, denounced all the criticisms at length in the House
of Commons. In particular, he dealt with the cost and emphasized that the price was not £2,000 but £120 for a 12-pounder
and £285 for a 40-pounder. Lord Herbert declared that 'we
had the best gun in the world'. And the Commander-in-Chief
of the Expeditionary Force in China continually praised
Armstrong's guns in public. But their words had no impact
on the critics. They could not—and would not be repulsed.
The *Mechanics Magazine* kept coming back to the subject
time and time again. Its reports, it said, were authentic and
accurate. The Armstrong lobby was trying to mislead the
public and to suppress vital evidence. 'Our accuracy has been
impugned and our facts questioned. We now confidently
appear before the public with our facts supported and our
reasonable predictions verified.' But were they and were their
arguments sound as well as sufficiently supported by evidence? What is one to make of their major criticism that the
Armstrong gun was continually undergoing change and
improvement? 'The inventor, in a short time, will scarcely
be able to recognize his own offspring.' Did they really expect
the gun, which if nothing else represented a radical departure
whether successful or not, would be perfect from the start?

Did they really expect that an inventor of any kind, never mind one as lively as Armstrong, would not want to make improvements?

The same mixture of half truths, false promises or specious deductions occurred in a series of letters from Captain Halsted. He reported that four of his Armstrong's large guns had broken down after firing only a few rounds and impugned the safety and endurance of the guns. He claimed that no 100-pound gun had up to that time been 'subjected to any representation of real action by fifty consecutive rounds of rapid fire.'[2] He said the guns were liable 'to choke up their shallow grooves with the lead covering of the missiles'. And he argued that the vent pieces were often unsatisfactory and blew off.

Point by point Armstrong answered the criticisms as best he could. He went into the performance of each of the four large guns, explaining their history in depth and showing how some small deficiencies had been overcome. He also appended an officially-compiled list of results showing that between 1856 and 1861 over 1,600 guns had been manufactured of which none had blown up and only 20 had been returned for repair. He also gave a list of prices, showing that the range extended from £120 for a 12-pounder to £650 for a 100-pounder.

Armstrong refuted Halsted's claim that no 100-pounder had been fired rapidly with fifty rounds. 'This is incorrect,' Armstrong replied simply. 'All descriptions of my guns have been fired fifty rounds at a time continuously with various degree of rapidity.' As for the lead covering choking up the shallow grooves in the barrel—'He is quite wrong.' With regard to the criticism of the vent pieces, the best answer again was the official Ordnance reports showing that of 1,492 manufactured, only five had blown away.

When he had dealt with the many criticisms, Armstrong turned to the personal element of the attacks that had been made. 'Captain Halsted does not write as a critic,' Armstrong declared, 'but as a downright uncompromising opponent. He acknowledges no one advantage in my system. The lightness of the guns, their precision of fire, their length of range, the extraordinary power of the shell in its different forms, as shown against every variety of object, are all passed over in silence while every appearance of failure (experimental or otherwise) is exaggerated and dressed up in highly coloured language, calculated to mislead the uninformed.'[3]

It might have misled them, it certainly entertained them and the papers enjoyed the arguments to the full and reported them at length. As *The Times* commented: 'Engineers are as irritable as poets and as jealous as rival beauties ... We confess to a suspicion that any other gun elevated, instead of the Armstrong gun, to the place of honour, would soon be attacked with as much vehemence as the present favourite. No man likes to see his own invention unnoticed while the invention of another brings him office and renown.' Of no one was this comment more true than Joseph Whitworth of Manchester.

## WHITWORTH ON THE ATTACK

He was especially vindictive and the feud between the two men at this time gives the eventual amalgamation of their two firms at the end of the nineteenth century an extraordinary sense of irony. By then Whitworth had been dead for ten years. Unlike Armstrong, Whitworth was able to combine his interest and his work from an early age. He started his working life at the age of 14, in 1817, in his uncle's cotton mill in Derbyshire. But he quickly developed an interest in engineering and left for Manchester where he worked for a number of machine making firms.

By 1833, when he was thirty, he set up in business on his own as a toolmaker. At first he worked on his own but the demand for machines from the booming railways or cotton industry provided plenty of growth.

He was not only interested in business as such but also in improving the quality of products. Between 1834 and 1849 he took out fifteen patents for new machine tools and gained a high reputation for superb products. By the 'fifties, he was one of the country's principal machine tool manufacturers. He was also noted for his pioneering work in developing extremely fine methods of measurement. He produced a machine which could measure to one two-millionth part of an inch, an outstanding achievement. The jury at an International Exhibition in 1862 commented that 'under the well-known and justly honoured name of Whitworth, were shown tools such as undoubtedly the world never saw before ... at least unsurpassed in general excellence of design and perfection of execution.' In 1856-7 he was President of the Institute of Mechanical Engineers. But perhaps even more important was his advocacy of a standard system of screw threads. At that time each manufacturer used his own methods. Within 17 years his work bore fruit. By 1858 standardized screw threads were in general use.

It was his outstanding work that led the Board of Ordnance to consult him during the Crimean War about the possibility of mass producing the Enfield rifle. He began a complicated series of tests which ended with him producing a Whitworth rifle. Although tests showed it to be superior to the Enfield rifle, it was not adopted by the Service.

Whitworth was also asked to rifle cannon. It was this introduction that set him on the road to developing his own system of artillery. Eventually he produced a system with three main characteristics. The first was that the barrel or rather the bore inside it was tapered from the breech to the muzzle. It was enclosed in a series of hoops, put on by hydraulic pressure rather than by heating and shrinking, which virtually formed a second tube. Then over that again another tube was placed. The thickness was thereby built up in three layers.

The second characteristic was the shape of the bore itself. Unlike Armstrong's which was circular and rifled, his was many-sided, rather like a kaleidoscope. The projectiles were the same shape so that they travelled down the bore in a steady way. With rifling, of course, the projectiles were spun around on the longitudinal axis.

The third important characteristic of the Whitworth system was the method of construction. He preferred a single type of metal for both barrel and gun. In the early days—that is around 1860—four years after Armstrong had developed his coil system—Whitworth favoured making the inner tube and outer hoops from cast-iron or brass. Later he made guns from a special type of mild steel which had been subjected to fluid compression.

The 'second father', Armorer Donkin.

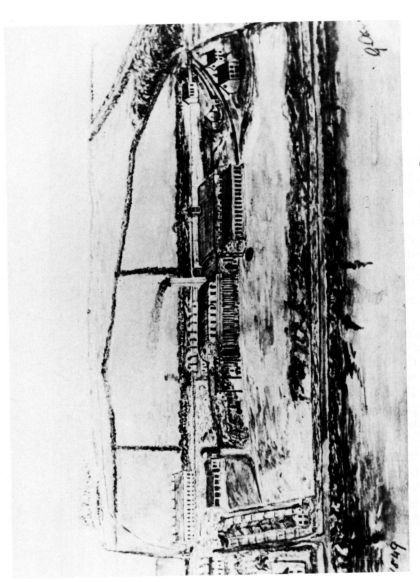

Sketch of Elswick Works in 1849, drawn by Mr George Stuart.

It was this system of construction, more than anything else, which bedevilled Whitworth's work. An account of 1864 stated: 'The manufacture of steel for ordance is in an uncertain and unsatisfactory state.' Armstrong himself declared: 'To make large guns on the principle of solid-forged tubes, either of steel or iron, I consider entirely out of the question because we can never penetrate the interior of the mass so as to discover the existence of flaws.'⁴ Of course, Armstrong was in the position of a special pleader.

It is worth noting that Alfred Krupps in Germany, who was working on the same problem, produced a tapered, silver bright steel gun in 1843 and another slightly bigger version in 1847. It was said to be 'a brilliant, technical success'.

But Armstrong disagreed with Krupp as well as Whitworth over the use of steel. Although differing in many other aspects, they agreed that steel was the right material. Armstrong on the other hand always advocated the use of wrought-iron in the form of welded coil for the main parts of a gun, limiting the use of steel to the bore where resistance to abrasion as well as tensile strength was required.

He took this view because whenever failure occurred, it almost invariably originated in the steel components. 'The conclusion at which I long since arrived,' he once said, 'is that although steel has much greater tensile strength than wrought-iron, it is less adapted to resist concussive strain. This conclusion is in strict harmony with the fact that armour-plates made of steel have proved on every occasion of their trial greatly inferior to plates of wrought-iron.'

He had carried out some experiments, immersing hot steel in a bath of oil, to try to reduce its fragility. The early tests proved very hopeful. The treated steel was very tough but when it was used as a target for a 68-pounder, it broke after only two shots. He pronounced steel a failure. He was prepared to admit that very strong guns could be made of steel but he was convinced that the number of failures and therefore the element of danger would be higher with steel than with wrought-iron.

In contrast, Whitworth's experience had not been a happy one. His very first guns were made of brass or cast-iron between the years 1856-58. They were only seven in all and they were supplied by the Government for him to rifle using his polygonal system. It was with these guns that he competed unsuccessfully against Armstrong in the 1858 trials. He also made three cast-iron guns in 1858 from blocks supplied by the Government. All three burst after firing a few rounds.

By 1860 he was starting to manufacture a whole gun in his own works at Openshaw in Manchester. His first two products—a 12-pounder and an 80-pounder—were made of steel hooped with wrought-iron. After sixty rounds, the 80-pounder burst. The following year the Government ordered twelve 12-pounders from Whitworth. This was a significant order for although the Government's main supply was from its own arsenal at Woolwich or from the Elswick works, it was prepared to place contracts elsewhere. Yet Whitworth continually complained of never being given a fair opportunity. Now he had been given a Government order but in vain. For his guns were condemned after only a short trial which showed they were not up to standard.

In 1861-62 he made another five guns using various systems. Only the fifth version—a 7-inch gun made for Whitworth at Woolwich using Armstrong's coil system and his own polygonal bore—produced results which could in any way compare with Armstrong's. By this time Armstrong had produced over 3,000 guns—Whitworth a mere unsuccessful handful.

The first Armstrong gun had been a built-up coil breech-loader with an inner tube of steel. It was rifled so that a soft-coated projectile would fit into the grooves as it travelled along the barrel. It was the coiled method of construction and the particular kind of rifling that provided the essence of Armstrong's work. Breech-loading, although important, was not fundamental. Indeed, Armstrong thought it would not be suitable for larger guns. With every increase in calibre, he thought the difficulties of breech-loading would increase. At about a calibre of 100-pounders the question became critical. Above that size, muzzle-loading was much better mainly because of the problems associated with the vent-piece.

Armstrong was in favour then of both breech-loading and muzzle-loading. He was not an out-and-out champion of breech-loading, as is sometimes believed. Muzzle-loading however presented a very great difficulty. In all rifled guns, the projectile must fit snugly into the barrel so that no vibration occurs as it makes its exit. It is relatively easy to achieve this standard with a breech-loading gun where the shot enters at the back of the barrel. But with muzzle-loading, it is not so obvious how to ensure that the shot enters easily yet issues from the gun tight. Armstrong solved the problem by shunt rifling.

Using these two methods, about 3,000 Armstrong guns were made between 1858 and 1863 in the following classifications:

| | |
|---|---|
| 12-pounders | 570 |
| 20-pounders | 257 |
| 40-pounders | 641 |
| 110-pounders | 799 |
| 150-pounders & over | 820 |

There were four main areas of difference between Armstrong and Whitworth: in rifling; in the type of ammunition used; in breech-loading; and, most important, in construction. Whitworth preferred guns built up from mild-steel while Armstrong favoured the welded wrought-iron coil. The House of Commons Committee of 1863 had no doubt about the system they preferred when they reported that they had no evidence that 'any other method of constructing rifled ordnance exists which can be compared to Mr Armstrong'.

Yet Whitworth continually and openly disparaged Armstrong's work and continually and successfully called for public enquiries into one aspect or another. Lord Rendel, whom we have quoted above, recalled: 'The most important of Lord Armstrong's rivals was undoubtedly Mr Whitworth, who had so successfully secured the attention of the authorities and of the public to his various inventions that not fewer than seven official committees had considered and reported on his projects from time to time, yet without giving him satisfaction or relieving the War Office of the pressure he and his friends were able to bring upon it ... Lord Torrington, a genial lord-in-waiting, was an active ally in society. Mr Whitworth took a house in Great George Street where he was always in attendance during the session to capture the suffrage of any member of either House of Parliament whom he could interest in his views.'[5] He became so persistent and had so many influential friends that eventually a special Armstrong and Whitworth Committee was appointed of high-ranking naval and military officers. This was to be the Enquiry that ended all Enquiries.

The Times, too, favoured the enquiry. 'We do not see how it can be denied that the present dissentients have made out a case for enquiry ... It is of the utmost importance to us that we should know the whole truth about the Armstrong gun, and this truth we shall never know until the gun has been subjected to every test without prejudice, favour or reserve.'[6]

Whitworth prepared for it very carefully, as Lord Rendel added: 'Not content with close scrutiny of the selection of members, Mr Whitworth demanded that he should have a special civilian representative on the committee. He nominated Mr Penn, the famous marine-engine builder, an irreproachable appointment. The War Office then called upon Lord Armstrong to appoint a civilian representative. After making all the resistance he could offer to the policy of such partisan representation, Lord Armstrong ... turned to me and asked me to give up my law work and join the Committee and I consented.'

## THE GOVERNMENT ENQUIRIES

The task was daunting, so complicated was the subject and so many were Whitworth's complaints. Whitworth complained that the 1858 trial was one-sided and unfair. He complained that he was not allowed to be present at the trial of his own gun. He complained that the Committee of 1858 did not visit his works as they had visited Armstrong's; that Armstrong, once he had been appointed Engineer of Rifled Ordnance, was not only allowed to advise on the work of other inventors but actually incorporated some of these other inventions into his own work in perfecting his own gun. Whitworth or his supporters then growing wilder and wilder in their accusations finally declared that Armstrong's work was based on other people's. Even the coiled tubing had been discovered earlier by a Captain Blakely.

The charges seemed to be endless. As soon as one was dealt with, another was put forward to keep the Committee busy. Lord Rendel wrote: 'The Armstrong and Whitworth Committee sat for three years. The range of its enquiry and the extent of its experiments make it quite unrivalled among artillery investigations in scope and thoroughness.' Whitworth's accusations were such that each one had to be carefully examined. For example, the Committee sifted thoroughly Whitworth's claim that he had not been invited to be present at the experiments on his own gun in 1858. It found that he had been notified on every occasion. Indeed the Secretary to the 1858 Committee on Rifled Cannon, Captain Andrew Noble, declared: 'I recollect distinctly his presence upon nearly all the occasions.'

The 1863 Committee next tackled the complaint that the 1858 Committee had not visited Whitworth's works at Openshaw, as it had visited Armstrong's works at Elswick. A member of the earlier Committee, Sir William Wiseman, explained why. 'When we first met, we thought that it would be necessary to visit both Sir William Armstrong's and Mr Whitworth's manufactories, in order to ascertain their method of manufacturing guns; but we only visited Sir William Armstrong's because we had no proposal from Mr Whitworth's before us for constructing guns at all.' In other words, Whitworth was not then manufacturing guns but simply rifling blocks under contract.

Thwarted here, Whitworth switched his ground and complained that Armstrong was given the opportunity to judge the work of his rivals after his appointment as Engineer of Rifled Ordnance. As Whitworth's principal supporter, Sir Emerson Tennent, put it in his book *The Story of the Guns*, published in 1864: 'He was thus constituted the confidential adviser of the Government, upon the discoveries of other inventors as well as of his own—a position of the utmost delicacy and difficulty and one in which it was hardly possible for its occupant to be regarded as an indifferent witness, or to escape the suspicion of being an interested umpire.'[7]

A little further on, Sir Emerson made a charge that was even more damning. 'It is said that some of the improvements brought forward by other inventors have been adopted by Sir

William Armstrong in perfecting the Government gun.' Exactly who was making such suggestions Sir Emerson did not say. He hid behind the phrase 'It is said'. He took careful pains to affirm that Armstrong was an honourable man and did not consciously abuse his position. But something much more than that was needed.

The 1863 Committee called for evidence from General St George, then Director of Ordnance, and asked him if Armstrong reported on the work of other inventors. 'He never does,' the General replied. 'Such a proposal is not submitted to him; it is invariably sent by the Director of Ordnance to the Ordnance Select Committee.' At another time, the Committee were told: 'Sir William Armstrong is not a member of the Ordnance Committee ... The great object of the reorganization of that Committee was to prevent the possibility of any inventor being on it.' There was therefore no opportunity for Armstrong to judge the work of other inventors.

Of course, his appointment as Engineer of Rifled Ordnance, or subsequently Superintendent of the Royal Gun Factory, and the large-scale manufacture of his guns provided advantages and experiences he would not have gained had he been unsuccessful at the trials. But it is going much too far to say, as his opponents did, that 'He was thus constituted the confidential adviser of the Government upon the discoveries of other inventors as well as his own.' Other statements were even harsher: 'Other inventors abstained from submitting their plans, through apprehension that they would fail to satisfy the Ordnance Select Committee, of which Sir William Armstrong was the constituted adviser, or else that their drawings and explanations might be made an unfair use of.'

When General St George was asked if he thought that other inventors would be deterred, he replied plainly: 'I do not see why inventors should be deterred. Sir William Armstrong is not referred to.'

'Sir William Armstrong never comes between the parties in any shape?'

'Never.'

General Peel of the War Office emphasized the same point, when he said of the Ordnance Committee: 'Sir William Armstrong is not a member of that Committee ... The great object of the reorganization of that Committee was to prevent the possibility of any inventor being on it.'

The evidence, once established, was clearly on Armstrong's side. But the constant smear campaign had its effect. Sir Emerson Tennent now disputed even Armstrong's original work. In particular, he declared that part of Armstrong's system, the coiled tubing, had been developed after a Captain Blakely had discovered a similar system. Tennent wrote: 'The Ordnance Select Committee, in 1861, reported to Lord Herbert that Captain Blakely's method and no other is the principle employed in the manufacture of the Armstrong guns.'

Now this statement by Tennent was simply untrue. The Ordnance Committee of 1861, after an interview with Captain Blakely, wrote: 'Captain Blakely on this occasion added nothing to what he has repeatedly urged in his publications, viz, that the true method of proceeding is to shrink one ring or coil of metal in another with a certain calculated tension, and he produced a pamphlet, published in 1858, as embodying his views. The Committee pointed out to him that this, and no other, is the principle employed in the manufacture of the Armstrong guns and it appears to them that whatever dispute there may be as to the originality or priority of invention, and the use of terms, between Captain Blakely and Sir William Armstrong, there is little or none in the matter of fact. Both make, or propose to make, strong guns in the same way; nor is the principle in any way new.'[8]

This is a very revealing statement. It shows very clearly that the Committee did not suggest, as Tennent claimed, that Captain Blakely's work preceded Armstrong's. The Committee in fact refused to discuss the question of priority. Furthermore, the Committee was discussing the subject of shrinking metal to give a 'certain calculated tension' and it rightly declared that this principle was not new. Armstrong's invention was not the shrinking of one layer of metal on another but the use of coiled tubing for the bore.

Whitworth and his supporters could here be seen in their full colours—misreporting, misquoting, misunderstanding in order to try to win points. When they were pinned down, they rapidly moved their attack elsewhere. But at last their tactics were becoming notorious and the Ordnance Select Committee took the unusual step of saying so.

The particular issue was Whitworth's 7-inch gun made at Woolwich on Armstrong's coil principle. Whitworth was to rifle it. But he wanted to gain the credit for making it too. He wrote to *The Times*: 'It is only due to myself to state that the Gun, besides being rifled on my system, was made to drawings supplied by me.' This assertion naturally took the Woolwich factory by surprise. The Secretary of State referred the matter to the Ordnance Committee. They reported: 'Such being Mr Whitworth's assertions, it is with unfeigned astonishment that the Committee have to report to the Secretary of State that they are not only not borne out by the facts of the case but that they are the reverse of the truth and they are at a loss to understand how a gentleman of Mr Whitworth's reputation could hazard them.'[9]

And so it went on. Charge after charge was knocked down to the ground but only after a long, painstaking and severely demanding enquiry. Lord Rendel: 'When we came to the report stage and for weeks and months together debated our report, I found myself overstrained. Practically, I led the case for Armstrong, while General Simmonds, who to the end of his life was my kind and good friend, led the case for Whitworth, and how we came to produce a report fairly capable of construction as generally favourable to Armstrong I can scarcely understand. But so it was and I may here declare unblushingly the plain fact that but for me the Whitworth case would have triumphed.'[10]

## OTHER CRITICS

As it was, Armstrong was vindicated. But it was a mere pyrrhic victory. For Armstrong had other enemies besides his rival manufacturers. These others were much more effective because they were often unknown. Snug inside the cosy cocoon of the Services, they could disparage any innovation as important as Armstrong's gun as being too far-reaching. The implications were manifold. Too many changes would be involved. Let us leave things as they were—and have been.

Armstrong's gun was difficult to operate, it was difficult to keep clean, it was difficult to repair. Even the intensity and accuracy of its fire-power was shown to be a disadvantage rather than a benefit. For a greater spread of shot was more likely to hit the enemy by chance. But with an extremely accurate weapon, you had to be sure your sighting was correct.

In addition, there was a groundswell of discontent about costs. It was said that the Elswick guns were too expensive, that too many overheads were being included in the cost of production. Indeed, some critics went so far as to suggest that Woolwich could produce the guns for only half the price.

This was extremely doubtful. But what was curious was that while Armstrong was continuously attacked, another private manufacturer—of cast-iron ordnance—received virtually no attention. As Lord Rendel said: 'It is somewhat singular that this fact never attracted public notice or criticism ... Considering the bitter contentiousness over the private manufacture of rifled ordnance, it is noteworthy that a single private firm should have enjoyed so great and profitable a monopoly without cavil. The fact is that nobody seemed to think there was an alternative to our 68-pounders and long 32's any more than our half-crowns and sixpences.'

Controversy which had gone on for so long was now getting out of hand. It would not die down but was fed continuously by new fuel. Finally, there came another element to destroy the whole project. The War Office found that its demands could now be adequately met by only one supplier. Alfred Cochrane commented: 'There was doubtless some justification for such a decision—with the normal demand for artillery as small as it was at that period, it was not possible to keep both arsenals at full swing; and sooner or later the crash was bound to come. But it is very difficult to understand why the decision was carried out as it was, to the thorough and complete exclusion of our works for many years from any share in the design and manufacture of English guns. Most of the real experts were then at Elswick and some advantage might, one would think, have been gained from occasionally employing their assistance. As it was Elswick was solemnly boycotted, the English authorities joyfully returned to an entirely primitive and obsolete system of artillery and it was not until 1878 that we succeeded in forcing on the notice of our own authorities a more modern type of gun and mounting.

Between 1859 and 1863 we received Government orders amounting to £1,063,000; between 1864 and 1878 our Government orders came to about £60,000.'

The blow was dramatic. From the country's point of view, a revolution in armaments was being undone. From Elswick's point of view, an enormous manufacturing capacity was having its basis removed. The likelihood was that the whole operation would come toppling to the ground, bringing the general engineering business with it. Armstrong had sincerely refused to exploit his patents. Instead he had handed them over to the Government. He had loyally refused to consider foreign orders. Instead he had said his factory would supply only the British Government. He had cut himself off from the new Elswick company, forsaking the opportunity to continue his research and development work. Instead he had become a Government employee and had turned the old-fashioned Woolwich gun foundry into a modern armament factory. And through all these years he had been caught up in controversy and criticism, most of which had been shown to be not only ill-founded but deliberately malicious. Now he was to be sacrificed, in an amazing transformation of patronage into ostracism.

## ARMSTRONG RETURNS TO ELSWICK

Armstrong took a natural step. He resigned from his Government position on 5th February 1863. He wrote to the Under-Secretary of State at the War Office that 'my friends who compose that company and who were induced by me to embark their capital in the undertaking, feel that they have a claim upon me to join their firm.' That is what he did. Shortly afterwards the Ordnance Company and the Engine Works were amalgamated under the title of Sir W. G. Armstrong and Company. A Deed of Co-Partnership for the amalgamation was signed on 1st January 1864. There were seven signatories: William Armstrong, George Cruddas, Richard Lambert, George Rendel, Andrew Noble, William Cruddas and Percy Westmacott.

The new company was in a critical position. The obvious way out was to sell the whole of the armament manufacturing capacity, plant and machines, to the Government. The entire capital spent had been £168,000. Allowing for depreciation, the company was willing to sell for £137,000. The offer was turned down out of hand. Instead, the Government offered to pay compensation, as the original contract stipulated. But the exact level of compensation was a matter for leisurely negotiation. Finally, the question was referred for arbitration to two well-known engineers, Mr T. E. Harrison of the North Eastern Railway Company and Mr H. Fenton, who acted on behalf of the Government. They agreed that compensation amounting to £65,000 should be paid. But the true value of this award to the company was probably another £20,000 since it was allowed to keep depreciated plant to this amount which the Government were entitled to take.

The new company was now free to look for a future if it could find one. As Armstrong himself said later: 'From that time, the firm had no alternative but to commence a new career, based on foreign support, and it was by that support —and not by Government patronage—that the Elswick Ordnance Works was established.' The rather sad undertone of that remark was as far as Armstrong would go in condemning the Government. Perhaps he hoped a new relationship could soon be created. Certainly he did not relish the future. When Stuart Rendel, who had played such a vital part in the three-year Government enquiry, urged Armstrong to turn to foreign buyers immediately, 'Lord Armstrong still looked upon the matter with much indifference.' He felt that although his Government contract had been terminated, he had received a knighthood and a well-paid office for three years. He could not so soon start to supply foreign powers. Rendel thought he could and should. Brazil was now anxious to buy arms. If Armstrong would not sell, Whitworth would. Rendel said: 'I looked upon the circumstance with much apprehension. Nothing could be more unfortunate for the reputation of the Armstrong gun than that it should be known by the British public that foreign Governments were preferring an English gun of a rival system.' Rendel further argued that if Armstrong did not take his opportunities 'new men would infallibly usurp his place.' Producing for foreign countries was not unpatriotic for those countries then became dependent on England for their armaments. This country would draw further ahead in the development of new techniques. Finally, Armstrong made a concession to Rendel. He said: 'If these are your opinions you are perfectly at liberty to try to give them effect and if you can obtain any orders for Elswick by all means do so and to make it worth your while we will give you five per cent commission upon the orders you bring us.' With that, Rendel set out on his roving commission.

## THE COMPANY AND ITS MEN

Meanwhile, Armstrong took up daily duties in the new firm. Basically, the organization was sound. A great deal of new investment had been undertaken recently. New land had been bought, new workshops opened, new machines installed, more workmen taken on. There were 3,800 employed, of which 3,000 were in the ordnance department, the biggest labour force in the area. The management structure was equally sound, made up of young but brilliant men like George Rendel, still only 30 years of age, who was in joint charge of the ordnance departments. There was Percy Westmacott, who was in charge of the engine works department. And above all there was Captain Andrew Noble, who was then just 32. With George Rendel, he was responsible for the ordnance departments. He had joined the firm in 1860 and been admitted to a partnership in 1861. Already he was beginning to display that mixture of scientific acumen and boundless energy that within a few years was to make him one of the world's greatest authorities on artillery. His dedication to Elswick and his contribution to Elswick were almost as great as Armstrong's himself. In his reckless pursuit of Elswick's progress, perhaps he was even more profligate. Social engagements, family life, even food or sleep were all a long way subservient to his work. The results were equally staggering. As one writer put it: 'The modern science of artillery is founded on Noble's work. His investigations form the basis of practically every modern theoretical treatise on internal ballistics.' By September 1863 he was publishing in the *Philosophical Magazine* his well-known 'Enquiry into the Ratio between the Forces tending to produce Translation and Rotation in the bores of Rifled Guns'.

It was a decisive piece of work in forcing forward the adoption of rifled ordnance to replace smooth-bore guns.

Noble's pioneering work allied to that of Armstrong himself, the employment of so many men, the investment in so much new capacity contrasted with the sudden cessation of orders. Here was an organization geared to efficient production—but with nothing to produce. On top of that Armstrong faced a new difficulty, a quarrel with his men. During the early years of the factory, relations between master and men had been cordial. As we have seen, Armstrong believed in taking in apprentices and training them his way. He could then rely not only on the employee's skill but also his loyalty. One out of many examples would be William Bradley, who served his apprenticeship at Elswick, became one of the best craftsmen, bored the first gun, and continued to serve the firm for 50 years. Promotion from within the company, based on courses organized by the foremen, the creation and expansion of a library, the provision of a school for workmen's children—all helped to produce a feeling of respect and admiration for Armstrong. The latent but evident feeling burst out with the founder's knighthood. The celebrations in February-March 1859 were spontaneous and deeply-felt expression of the men's attitudes.

## THE FIRST LABOUR TROUBLE

But by the early 1860's a sea-change had occurred. There were a number of reasons why. The company was now bigger than ever. Communications inside the works became a problem in itself, although one to which management paid scant regard, if indeed they considered it a problem at all. Armstrong himself was no longer known to the men personally as he once had been. He had spent the past three years in London, visiting Elswick only occasionally. A new structure of middle and senior management had been built in. Above all, the company could no longer be insulated, as it had been in its early days, from the general economic conditions of the day. When bad times occurred, the management started to take the same action as managements elsewhere, laying workers off and cutting wages. The hope was that such action would reduce the firm's costs so that the price to the customer could be reduced as an inducement to him to begin placing orders again. So often, however, this type of action annoyed and indeed angered the men and the loss of loyalty more than offset any reduction in costs.

Armstrong's was now to enact this classical scenario. Towards the end of May 1862, the men in the armament section were told by their foremen that they were to be paid six days' pay for five night shifts. At the time, shift work was paid for at time and a half. In other words, five night shifts would be worth seven and a half days' pay. The new arrangement represented a reduction of twenty per cent. In addition, labourers' wages were to be cut by two shillings a week. The men were given no reason for the action although it would be clear enough. But they naturally deplored being treated in this way after the relationship they had been used to. They had no union, indeed they had not felt the need of one. But now conditions seemed to be changing.

To register their objection to the new arrangement and the way it was broached, they decided to leave work at 3.30 p.m. on Friday, 30th May. The management posted a notice that those who did so could call for their dismissal notices and final wages, the following day. Between fifty and sixty mechanics and a considerable number of general workers from one particular workshop left early and received their dismissal notices the next day. According to the *Newcastle Chronicle*, the majority of other workers 'identified themselves in principle, though not in practice' with those who left work.

The men had no union organization to help them but they did have a sense of comradeship. They decided to hold a general meeting at the Music Hall in Nelson Street on the Monday evening. About a thousand men turned up. According to a local newspaper, the meeting was of 'a somewhat boisterous character' but 'evidently composed of highly intelligent men'. No doubt that was a comment on the fact that most of the men wanted to resolve the question as quickly as possible. This attitude was exemplified by a mechanic called John Curry. He declared that there was 'too much suspicion among the workers', that no one should have stopped work without consulting all their colleagues. He also proposed that they should 'appoint four intelligent workmen to draw up a petition to be presented to their employers'. This was agreed but other workers were determined on a show of force. About 250 men went on strike, emptying two shops, while James Beattie, James Blackney, John Curry and Charles Bell started to draw up a petition. They had it ready in two days. On Wednesday, 4th June, they presented it to Captain Noble. It read:

'To the Owners and Managers of the Elswick Ordnance Works,
Gentlemen,
Agreeable to resolutions passed at a public meeting of the workmen in your employ, held in the Music Hall on Monday evening last, we, your petitioners, fully believing that the present disputes are alike detrimental to the interest of the employers and employed, would beg humbly to approach you as mediators; and while we have no desire to intervene between master and men, where any arrangements have been entered into, we entrain the hope that our conduct will merit your approval.

We would humbly submit a few considerations which have influenced us in our present proceedings. We believed the men committed an error in making a hasty determination to leave their work and this may have caused some unnecessary irritation to their employers. We would, however, plead on their behalf the short period allowed them to consider the new rule, and likewise, the large diminution of their wages ... was an important matter with them.

Trusting you will reconsider the case of those who have recently been discharged from your employ and receive them on such terms as they enjoyed heretofore or such as will tend to conciliate and inspire confidence in your good intentions towards them. We also embody in this petition the wish of the foundry men that their condition also receive your considerations as far as the proposed reduction in wages.'

The tone of conciliation, indeed humility, that runs through the letter was extraordinary. The men could not have been more diplomatic in their language or more persuasive in stating their objections. Yet to no avail. Noble, who was already acquiring that omniscient air for which he was later to become legendary, refused to budge an inch. The reductions were required because of the falling order book, he told the men. They had to be accepted. There was no alternative. Equally he could not make any general offer to re-employ those who had discharged themselves. Individual cases would be considered however. Faced with such an implacable employer, the men capitulated. At the end of the week, that is on Friday, 6th June, those who wanted to return to work and were offered re-employment did so. But like everyone else, they had to accept lower wages. Noble had won but in doing so he was storing up trouble for the future. One cannot help wondering what would have been the outcome had Armstrong taken a more active interest in this incident. Could he have prevented a fissure developing which was to grow wider and wider?

Certainly he tried later to patch things up or perhaps to pretend they had not happened. For in early August he invited the 270 members of the Elswick Engine Works Literary and Mechanics Institute to 'a most excellent tea' in his new banqueting hall at his house in Jesmond. Armstrong seems to have spent most of the time showing off a small ornament. When it was opened, a little bird 'shook its wings, moved its head and, after singing for a minute or two, disappeared'. But however much he tried, relationships between him and his men were changing, as we shall see later.

THE BRITISH ASSOCIATION IN NEWCASTLE

These four years, by far the most turbulent of his career, offered at the end at least one glorious consolation. For in 1863, when the British Assocation for the Advancement of Science held its annual meeting for only the second time in Newcastle, Armstrong was elected President. 'I esteem it,' he said, 'the greatest honour of my life.' No doubt he felt that here was a reward that could have no unhappy and unexpected repercussions. He threw himself into the preparations with whole-hearted vigour. Here he would be back in his own world with his own kind of men.

Elswick shipyard at its peak at the turn of the century.

The first five pounder-gun, now in the Museum of Science and Engineering, Newcastle.

His inaugural address, wide-ranging and forward-looking in content and simple and lucid in style, was one of the best he ever delivered. He talked of the rapid developments of the recent past and the enticing prospects for the imminent future.

'A quarter of a century has elapsed since the Association assembled in this town,' he said, 'and in no former period of equal duration has so great a progress been made in physical knowledge. In mechanical science ... the progress made since 1838 has no parallel in history.'[11] As his main example, he talked of what had happened in the development of railways. When coal was first moved from a pit to the river Tyne for shipment, it had to be done by pack-horse, he said. The horse could manage three hundredweights. Then carts were introduced, increasing the load to seventeen hundredweights. The introduction of wooden rails allowed loads up to forty-two hundredweights. Iron rails allowed a further increase. Finally, the arrival of the locomotive took the tonnage up to its current level. Over two hundred hundredweights could now be conveyed at a cost of fuel scarcely greater than the cost of hay needed by a horse. 'How promptly,' reflected Armstrong, 'the inventive faculty of man supplies the device which the circumstances of the moment require. The seeds of invention exist, as it were, in the air, ready to germinate whenever suitable conditions arise.'

Railways led him on to coal, the great natural resource of the North East of England. He talked of the contribution of the Davy lamp to the progress of the mining industry. He talked of the recent experiments which had determined the materials of which the sun was composed and of the discovery of the dynamic theory of heat. The latter was, he said, 'the most important discovery in the present century'. He looked at meteorology and declared that many developments were needed to make it a science. He talked of the physical methods of writing and complained how inefficient they were. And he disagreed with Darwin's theory of natural selection. It was all most entertaining and the delegates expressed their approval by 'thunder-like applause', when he sat down.

They must have been equally impressed by the signs of unprecedented industrial activity they could see in the region. Never had the north known a more active period of change, of new ideas, new industries, new towns and new people. William Gladstone, then Chancellor of the Exchequer, paid the area full tribute when he visited Newcastle in 1862. He said: 'I know not where to seek, even in this busy country, a spot or district in which we perceive so extraordinary and multifarious combination of the various great branches of mining, manufacturing, trading and shipbuilding industry, and I greatly doubt whether the like can be shown, not only within the limits of this land, but upon the whole surface of the globe.'

In paying this fulsome tribute, Gladstone was indirectly applauding Armstrong as much as anyone for even remembering the railway-building Stephensons, he had probably made a bigger contribution to the industrial and scientific progress of the area than anyone else. But now the future seemed to be in doubt. Would it be possible to switch quickly to foreign orders? Would there be at least a temporary recession, a paying-off of valuable workpeople, a closing of part of the works and a temporary loss on the substantial capital investment? Armstrong put a brave face on things but this new era in his career was opening with many uncertainties.

# CHAPTER FIVE

## THE 'NEW CAREER'

ARMSTRONG was now 53. Although this was no great age—indeed he was just a little over half way through his life for he lived to be 90—and although he was to retain for many years yet his physical and mental energies, he seemed to have lost some of his old drive. The sheer determination that had produced an armament revolution wilted a little. He left more to his able lieutenants, Captain Andrew Noble and George Rendel, who was later joined by his two brothers Stuart and Hamilton. Hamilton Rendel, who joined the firm in 1866, was a born engineer, a brilliantly inventive man but a very shy one. His great triumph was the design and construction of Tower Bridge in London.

There were also Mr George Cruddas, and his son William, Percy Westmacott, Colonel Dyer and others. Instead of the central driving force, working with single-minded dedication late into the night, he became the judicious Committee chairman. He still tended to take the important decisions but he no longer made the physical commitment he had once done or that Andrew Noble was now doing and was to continue to do all his life. Increasingly Armstrong left the day-to-day running of the business to others and returned either to the peace of his laboratory or to the creation of a new home at Cragside on the moors above Rothbury in mid-Northumberland. Of course, the past few years had proved a serious drain on his resources. The constant swirl of controversy had taken its toll. He knew that a 'new career' based on foreign orders rather than Government contracts, was called for but his heart was not altogether in it. According to a close colleague, he attached 'little importance' to the prospect of foreign orders.

As he and his associates now surveyed the world market, they recognized that they had three principal rivals.

At home, there was Joseph Whitworth and Company of Manchester. Although the firm was much smaller than Armstrongs, it had already entered the overseas market. For the Brazilian Government had placed a number of contracts with it in 1862-3. This was at a time when the British Government had begun to tail off its orders to Elswick but refused to allow the firm to break its agreement to supply no one but itself. Brazil had in fact applied to Armstrongs but the War Office refused to give permission. Whitworth also gained orders from both sides in the American Civil War, from New Zealand, France and other countries.

The main competition, however, came from abroad. In France, there was the Schneider family at Le Creusot. In 1836, Eugene Schneider and his brother Adolphe had bought the rather dilapidated gunworks at Le Creusot which had been created by Louis XVI. The brother's initial interest had been in railways and steam power. Within a few years they turned the factory into one of the most modern engineering works in Europe. But then, with the development of new methods of steel manufacture, Eugene began to envisage the possibility of armament manufacture. Why armaments specifically, we do not know. Perhaps, like Armstrong, it was the chance occurrence of the Crimean War. Whatever it was, he and his son Henri began to swing the company into the new activity of producing cannons. In the final third of the nineteenth century, Schneider became one of the world's most powerful arsenals.

But, of course, the real competition for Armstrong was provided by Alfred Krupp* in Prussia. Indeed, from the mid-1860's onwards, Krupp and Armstrong bestrode the international armaments business with Scheiders and Whitworth dividing the rest of the orders. Alfred Krupp was a brilliant, unbearable industrialist from Essen who in the mid-1860's had just earned the nickname of the 'Cannon King', a phrase so apt that it was to be handed down from generation to generation. Krupp preceded Armstrong in drawing attention to the extraordinary dichotomy that was to exist for the arms manufacturer.

For while arms and armaments represented the height—

* He preferred the English spelling of his name.

or perhaps the depths—of nationalistic ambitions, they also flourished as an international business. Krupp had sold weapons of war to Belgium, Holland, Austria, Spain, Switzerland and particularly to Russia, which placed an order worth £150,000 with him in August 1863. Of his workforce of 10,000, the majority, he said, were working for Russia. Krupp had even sold arms to the British Government or rather to the Admiralty which had to keep extremely quiet about the deal. Krupp saw no dangers. Here were straightforward, unsophisticated commercial transactions. He even wrote to Crown Prince Friederich Wilhelm of Prussia quite openly about his intentions. 'Why should not England, in urgent circumstances, obtain the material from her friends abroad until her own industries can make it?'

Krupp argued that to keep his factory busy he needed foreign buyers. Only in time of war would he be able to rely wholly on the domestic market. In the meantime he wanted to sell to friendly countries. This argument, put over so persuasively at a time when *laissez-faire* economic freedom was at its height, ignored of course one simple question. Who were your real friends and how long would they remain so?

To Krupp such thoughts, if they occurred, were of academic interest. Their business was to make guns and to sell them to anyone who would buy. And many people were starting to buy. Krupp put on a dazzling display of his military capability at the London exhibition of 1862. It led *The Times* to comment: 'We congratulate Krupp on the pre-eminent position which he occupies.' Armstrong could only take solace in misfortunes. When he heard that a Krupp cannon had exploded during trials he told his works manager, George Rendel, it had done so 'with a vengeance, flying into a thousand pieces. All the fragments were sound so that the failure was purely due to the intrinsic unsoundness of the material. I have had this nice piece of news conveyed to Lord Grey' (under-Secretary for War).

There was no doubt that Krupp set the pace. He had been in business longer than Armstrong, even though he was two years younger. But the early days were much harder for him. The eldest boy in a family of three sons and a daughter, he had taken over the crumbling family business in 1826 at the age of 14. His father, Friederich, had turned a large family fortune into dust and a prosperous cast-steel factory into a bankrupt outfit with just seven workers. His final two years were ones of utter humiliation which he spent lying on a sick-bed in the hovel of a home. He died at the age of 39.

So while William George Armstrong was completing his education at Dr Bruce's Academy in Percy Street, Newcastle, a thousand miles to the south east in Essen, Prussia, one of those dramatic scenes which the industrious Germans like to paint about their leaders was taking place. A remarkably composed, indeed even ruthlessly composed, boy of 14 was surveying the mess he had inherited. In later years this scene was to be glorified in German folk-lore. It was not quite so throbbing at the time yet it was still dramatic enough. The boy was very tall and thin, he was good with his hands and above all he had almost limitless determination. He never gave in. These qualities were even then apparent. Others developed later—his tormented mind, his unbelievable eccentricities. For example, he thought the smell of horse manure nurtured the imagination. Years later when he built himself a mad castle of 300 bedrooms, he put his own room immediately above the stables and bored a tube through the ceiling so that the pungent smell would filter in.

For four years the boy Krupp managed to hang on to the business while he tried to rediscover his father's formula for cast-steel, which had disappeared with him. Finally, in 1830, he succeeded. That year, too, the firm managed to break even. It was down to just five workers now. But that was the end of the decline. From that point on the upward path began. Progress was slow, to be sure, and Alfred, so brilliant in some ways and so naïve in others, made many mistakes. But, in essentials, he proved himself right and resolute.

By 1834 his workforce had jumped to sixty-seven. He was producing good quality steel for making tools or cutlery rolls and the orders were flowing in. But financially difficulties remained. Even as late as 1848 when his mother left him the works in her will, he described it as the 'wreck of a factory'.

During these years Alfred had taken up a hobby, forging a gun. By 1843, after seven years work, it was ready—a tapered, silver-bright barrel. a most beautiful piece of craftsmanship.

But when he tried to sell it he found no takers. For, as Armstrong was to find too, the profession of arms was sunk deep in the mud of the past. In some branches, nothing had changed for centuries. Gunpowder had been unchanged for 600 years, heavy weapons for 400. Some refinements had been made but they were small.

Armourers were ignorant of chemical and metallurgical principles. Weapons exploded. Gunpowder failed to ignite. Cast-iron had been used for many years but it still remained brittle. Wrought-iron was too soft. Bronze was the safest metal even though it was so heavy and expensive. Against these traditional materials and blocked minds, Krupp's cast-steel three-pound cannon had no chance. He exhibited his gun at the Crystal Palace world fair in 1851 but although it attracted much attention, it still did not find a buyer.

In 1852 Krupp therefore decided to give it away. He sent it to the King of Prussia who was so impressed he installed it in his palace and the following year made a visit to the Krupp factory. Alfred Krupp was pleased. He felt he had found a new sales gimmick. He decided to donate guns to Switzerland, Austria and Russia. And at last Russia bit. She decided to buy a Krupp cannon. Suddenly the walls of resistance broke. In 1859 the Prussian War Office ordered 312 six-pounders, worth £30,000. But even then Alfred Krupp's joy was not unalloyed. For the War Office refused to accept rifling in the barrels, and even more exasperating, it also refused to accept breech-loading, with which he had been experimenting.

But nevertheless the breakthrough had been made and in quick succession, just before Armstrong entered the international market, Krupp sold guns to Russia, Belgium, Holland, Spain, Switzerland, Austria and even England. He was now on his way.

The sale to England was done behind Armstrong's back. As soon as he heard of the order, he had appealed to the Government, but the Admiralty secretly bought barrels from Krupp.

During the frustrating fifties Krupp's factory had been kept going—and indeed expanding—by his invention of seamless railway wheels. This invention turned into an enormous business as railways spread their tentacles over Europe and America. Krupp himself recalled in later life: 'It was only through the manufacture of tyres (railway wheels) under the protection of our patents, that the works were able to make enough profit to lay down the gunmaking plant.' Railways subsidized arms just as in the same way hydraulic machinery and other engineering equipment helped to subsidize the early years for Armstrong.

Krupp was now one of the world's greatest industrialists. He played the part. He dominated his workpeople, whom he regarded as his personal property. There were notes and rules about everything, enforced by fines. He had his own factory police force. Yet still he was not satisfied. 'I want once more to call attention to ... idleness and waste of time, such as can be seen daily.' he complained in one of his never-ending torrent of notes. As he grew older and his works became even bigger, the orders and the demands grew more excessive, even more authoritarian.

### FIRST FOREIGN ORDERS

This was the man with whom Armstrong now started to do battle. His first success came from America where the Civil War was in progress. The northern states wanted to buy a few heavy guns for naval use. Their Minister in London, Mr Adams, consulted Mr Scott Russell, the shipbuilder and naval architect. In great secrecy, Scott Russell communicated with Armstrong and the order was arranged. It was Elswick's first foreign order and the whole negotiation and the eventual manufacture and despatch of the guns had to be done in the greatest confidence.

This order later led to a bitter dispute between Armstrong and Russell and a full-scale enquiry by the Council of the Institution of Civil Engineers. What happened was this. In January 1864 Russell placed orders for guns on behalf of the State of Massachusetts. The amount of the order, £14,422, was to be paid to Armstrong as various parts of the work were completed. Only £8,734 was received. Yet the American Minister said that the full amount had been paid out to Russell. An American officer enquired into the situation and reported to Armstrong that 'Mr Russell had confessed to him that he had used the money for his private purpose and was unable to refund.'[1]

Three years later, in early 1867, the matter came before the Council of the Institution of Civil Engineers. They held an enquiry during which Russell complained of Armstrong's 'gross misrepresentation'. He had tried to help Armstrong and this was his reward. Armstrong had come to him when 'the Elswick Works were standing nearly empty and out of work' and asked him 'as a great favour ... to help ... to restore work to Elswick and credit to Sir William Armstrong.'

Russell said he agreed to place orders for five large cannon to be completed within a specific period. Armstrong failed to complete the work on time and this meant Russell's contract with his American client was also broken. 'Here, perhaps, the transaction should have ended. I ought to have refused altogether to have anything more to do with Sir William or his guns.' But Russell claimed he bought four of the guns himself, paying by cash, but refused to accept the other. 'Sir William tried to force my acceptance,' but failed. He also refused to hand over the guns that were paid for. Both parties remained adamant and stuck to their positions to the end. Russell's reputation by this time, however, was notorious. The Enquiry had no hesitation in coming down on Armstrong's side and the Council of the Institution decided to expel Russell from membership. But Armstrong never got the money that was owing to him.

The southern states of America also placed orders, through Stuart Rendel, the barrister who had represented Armstrong at the official enquiry in 1862-3 and who had now been given a roving sales commission. Rendel was a very close friend of Mr Gilliat, the London banker for the southern states. He arranged a meeting in Paris between Rendel and the military agents of the southern states. As a result, more orders came to Elswick.

Rendel proved a good salesman. Whether it was the incentive of a five per cent commission on all orders placed through him or whether it was his own shrewd handling of negotiations, Rendel certainly proved invaluable to the firm. But he himself felt his role was only a temporary one. 'I was not an inventor or even an engineer and I was invading a citadel jealously garrisoned by military officers and officials. I was also always sundering the bough on which I sat in regard to Elswick. For, as soon as I had gained a foreign convert and he or his emissary had reached Elswick, I was of necessity more or less superseded by my practical Elswick colleagues. Once I had established relations between Elswick itself and any foreign government, my duties became distinctly subaltern.'[2] To overcome this feeling he suggested to Armstrong that he should join the firm and become the London manager. Armstrong agreed and sold him a one-twenty-fifth share in the partnership for £19,600.

With this extra security, Stuart Rendel's flair for negotiation produced even better results. He became acquainted in some way with a Captain Albini of Italy, then an Italian Naval Attache, living in humble lodgings on the other side of Blackfriars Bridge. 'I used my acquaintance with him for the furtherance of the first order for guns from the Italian Government. For some years I was the sole channel of communications between Captain Albini and Elswick.' This was the start of a long series of orders from Italy. The connection eventually led to the formation of an Armstrong factory in Italy, as we shall see later.

Stuart Rendel used another acquaintance, Lord Goschen, to secure orders from Egypt. He learned from Goschen that the Khedive wanted armaments to secure his independence and that he had sent a personal friend to Europe in great secrecy to negotiate contracts. Goschen acted as an intermediary and soon negotiations were taking place. 'The result,' wrote Rendel, 'was that Efflatoun Pasha placed himself entirely in the hands of the Elswick firm and for some time I was the intermediary through whom his very important orders for guns were placed.'

As usual, an important flow of orders like this did not prevent Rendel from also opening negotiations with countries that were or could be enemies, like Turkey. At that time, Turkey had a number of orders with British shipbuilders for warships. It now wanted armaments to be mounted on them. Rendel was happy to supply them.

Other social friends helped him to gain orders in other countries. There was Mr George Gibbs, a partner in the South American firm of Antony Gibbs and Son. He naturally knew the South American market intimately and provided Rendel with introductions which led to orders from the Chilean Government. In Russia and Austria, he had personal contacts himself in the right quarters. Indeed, he was even allowed to sit upon artillery committees and observe artillery experiments. He did the same in Vienna. But in neither country was he successful. 'I found the Krupp interest too powerfully installed, politically and otherwise, for successful opposition.' Krupp also managed to thwart at the last moment what would have been a great coup for Rendel, an order from Prussia itself. He had obtained a provisional order for the armament of one of Prussia's earliest ironclad warships, the *Koenig Wilhelm*. Rendel was even invited to the launch ceremony as the representative of the firm that was to supply the armaments. He must have thought the deal was now but a formality. But even at such late moments Krupp never accepted defeat. Despite the international nature of his business, he believed that the Prussian market was exclusively his. It was not only a question of national honour but of his personal honour, indeed the two were indisolubly mixed. Hearing of the prospective order for Armstrongs, Krupp appealed to Bismarck himself in overtly emotional terms. The negotiations were stopped.

Krupp did not need to use such pitiful tactics for he was now immensely successful but it was part of the nature of the man. As he grew older, his eccentricities became even more noticeable and unbearable. He was now only in his fifties but he was unpredictable in the extreme; petty, spiteful, dictatorial in a way that even the haughtiest industrialist in England would not have dared to emulate. Armstrong by comparison, was so normal. He was not given to fits of outrageous passion, to sulking for months on end, to blaming his lieutenants excessively for any small mistakes or to witholding praise where it was due. Nor did he treat his wife like a chattel.

Now, in the late 1860's, these two men of such contrasting personalities, dominated the world armament business. Krupp was established in Belgium, Holland, Austria, Spain and above all Russia and Prussia. Armstrong had good clients in Egypt, Turkey, Italy, Denmark and South America, particularly in Chile and Peru. Krupp was always slightly ahead but Armstrong ran him a close race.

Krupp had the advantage of domestic orders as well as foreign sales. Armstrong had to rely wholly on overseas buyers. In fact, from 1863 to 1878 orders from the British Government came to only £60,000.

But despite his enormous success, Krupp remained petty, selfish and unscrupulous. In 1868 he heard that the navy of the new Germany was considering placing an order with Armstrong. Krupp immediately set off for Russia, his 'great supporter' to seek compensation in 'enormous orders'. He was also after something else; testimonials from Russian admirals to the excellence of his guns. He got them too and laid them before the King. He also wrote letters endlessly. 'That equal justice has not been meted out to me, the native manufacturer, is the thing of which I have to complain ... That the Royal Prussian Navy should not draw its guns from abroad so long as it has an opportunity of obtaining better guns at home, is for me much more a matter of honour than of financial interest ... Such a proceeding on the part of Prussia would be, more than anything else, an exposure of the Essen establishment to humiliation in the eyes of the whole world'. The extraordinary combination of emotion and shrewdness, so typical of the man, convinced not only the King but Armstrong's men. They left, never to try again.

## NAVAL SHIPBUILDING AND ARMAMENTS

A new stimulus for armament manufacturers was now emerging—naval work. So far, attention had been largely centred on land-based guns but with the development of iron shipbuilding and the introduction of ironclads into the navies of various countries, a new type of armament was needed. A closer working arrangement between shipbuilder and armament maker was also foreseen. Armstrong began to look around.

Three firms were considered: the Naval Construction and Armaments Company of Barrow; Charles Mitchell and Co. of Low Walker on Tyne; and the Palmer Brothers of Jarrow. The Naval Construction and Armament Company at Barrow, although very experienced, was too far away to provide all the advantages that were being looked for. The choice fell, therefore, between the two Tyneside companies. That formed by the Palmer Brothers in 1851 was by far the bigger and more successful. The two brothers, of whom Charles Mark Palmer was the more important, had taken over a small yard which had been building frigates for the navy since the turn of the century. They had then indulged in a wild gamble of producing the world's first motor-powered coal-carrying ship. The gamble lay in the cost—£10,000 as against £1,000 for a convention sail collier. But the gamble succeeded. For the motor-powered vessel could get through more than ten times the work of the sailing vessels. Palmers flourished; the North East coal industry was saved from the competition put up by the Midland coal-fields linked to London by the new railway system; the village of Jarrow expanded into a major industrial centre. During the Crimean War, Palmers were given an emergency order by the Admiralty to produce an ironclad vessel. The company finished the order in three months and incorporated a new technique of rolled-iron in the vessel, the *Terror*. This was the first North East iron warship. She had a displacement of 2,000 tons, mounted sixteen 300-pound guns and was propelled by engines of 200 h.p. The hull was built of iron in the ordinary way except that the sides sloped to 25 degrees and were protected from shot by iron armour plates four inches thick, backed by six inches of teak, all of which was bolted to the main structure. The war was over before the *Terror* was commissioned, however. This meant that Palmer's enterprise in using rolled-iron plates could not be tested in action. In consequence, the Admiralty was prepared to give them only half the credit to which they thought they were due. For while complimenting them on the speed of delivery, their Lordships refused to accept the validity of their rolled plates experiments. They had to pay for most of the research and development work out of their own pockets to prove their theory. 'The commercial men of this country have set the Admiralty a signal example of industry and enterprise,' Charles Mark Palmer said. It was 1862 before his company built another naval vessel but from then on they formed an important part of the business.

Armstrong knew Palmer well and one might have thought that his firm would have been the obvious choice for the new arrangement. But Armstrong favoured the Low Walker yard of Dr Charles Mitchell, which had begun operations in the same year as the Jarrow enterprise. Mitchell was a Scotsman, now in his late forties. As a young man he had travelled down to Tyneside after serving his time as an assistant draughtsman in a shipyard at Aberdeen. Within a few years he had started his own business.

It was with his firm that Armstrong signed an agreement in 1867. Mitchell's yard would build the vessels and Armstrong's works would manufacture and fit the weapons. George Rendel was put in charge of the new venture and it was to his design that the early ships were built. His specification included a light draught, no great speed and a single powerful gun. The first order come from the Admiralty and was delivered in 1868. This was H.M.S. *Staunch* described as a 'floating gun carriage with fair speed and great handiness'. Its speed, in fact, was between seven and eight knots, it had a displacement of 160 tons and a nine-inch muzzle loading gun. This prototype proved successful. In the next ten years, twelve similar gunboats were ordered by the Admiralty and the same standard design was used for orders from Italy, Brazil and Chile. This was the start of a huge naval output for Governments all over the world. Within the next quarter century Armstrong was to become the country's most important naval shipbuilder, as we shall see later.

Throughout these past fifteen years, Armstrong's main interest as an armament designer and manufacturer had been in guns and heavy ordnance. But equally dramatic changes had occurred in the field of small arms, especially with the introduction of automatic weapons. Three men were largely responsible for this revolution: Richard Gatling, Hiram Maxim and Thorsten Nordenfeld. Gatling, who was six years younger than Armstrong, had had his interest aroused in armaments by the American Civil War. In 1862 he produced a machine gun which consisted of a number of barrels which rotated around a central shaft. It was capable of firing up to 350 rounds a minute.

## THE GATLING GUN

In 1870 Armstrong became the British licensee for the Gatling Gun Company. Under this, Armstrong's factory would immediately produce 200 Gatling guns at a price of £103 each. The agreement proved very beneficial but by 1873 Armstrong's were complaining that they needed an extra incentive for pushing sales. John Love, the chairman of the Gatling Gun Company, agreed that the company should receive five per cent commission from the selling price. Love wrote: 'Realizing the importance of pressing the sale of the "Gatling" at this time we cheerfully make this concession in the hope and expectation that it may indemnify you for such extra exertions.'[3]

By 1875, the price and the commission was revised again. Armstrong was to be paid £113 for the 0.50 calibre gun and £150 for the 0.65 calibre. He was also to receive five per cent extra for re-tooling required and a five per cent commission on any orders gained by himself. The selling price at that time was £205 for the smaller version and £265 for the larger, a very handsome profit for the American company. Business was better than ever. Edgar Welles, the company secretary, wrote to Stuart Rendel, the head of Armstrong's London office in 1876: 'I have just returned from a somewhat protracted absence in Washington, where, by the way, I found the reputation of our gun higher than ever and secured further orders ... We are just now experimenting on some slight changes in our model of the gun and if they seem advantageous will forward drawings to you.' By now the Gatling Gun had been adopted by the British Government although it had not been decided exactly what role it would play. The gun, which could fire four to five hundred rounds a minute, was also being used by the Navy as a new armament for ships. In the first place only flagships and large ironclads were supplied with them but later they were used in vessels of the corvette class.

In 1877 the Gatling Gun Company introduced a new model. The 'improvement, although changing the appearance of the gun but little, makes it work perfectly,' Edgar Welles wrote to Stuart Rendel. And he suggested an exhibition, or a series of experiments at Woolwich.

Rendel pointed out that since he believed he was on the brink of receiving new orders from the British Government, the appearance of a new model would only delay the signing of a contract, and would in any case lead to a request for expensive new trials. Welles replied that he was willing to leave the question 'to the good judgement of your firm'. Welles added; 'I think myself that everyone who examines the new models will be greatly pleased with them but I do not think any trials could or should follow in England. The guns are the same as in use now, only with modifications, simplifications and improvements.'

Welles' views were vindicated a few months later at the naval engagement in Peru where the Gatlings were used to good effect. He wrote to Rendel knowing 'how much it will interest you and how glad you will be to hear of the good work of the Gatlings in the way you have so often predicted.'

By 1878 new competition was beginning to appear. The British Admiralty had carried out tests with the Swedish mitrailleuse and found 'that it compares favourably with the Gatling Gun in their opinion'. But Welles declared: 'We think not a single officer in the English service has yet seen a new model Gatling'. He called urgently for new trials at Woolwich, Chatham or anywhere. Rendel tried to soothe Welles but he remained anxious. 'You may remember, I pointed out in conversation, the danger from competing guns; but you assured me, the Gatling gun, being the adopted gun, could not be superseded, save by regular competitive trials and adoption. But we must look at the situation now.'

A few months later Welles wrote that he had heard the Admiralty had ordered some of the Swedish guns. 'We are at a loss to understand how it is received with favour by your naval authorities.' Later he was even blunter: 'To be perfectly frank, I should also say that much comment has also come to us on the differences in manufacture of the Gatling gun at your works at Colts—and not in your favour.'

By the end of 1878 the Committee of Artillery had decided to hold trials with the Gardner, Hotchkiss, Nordenfeld and Gatling guns to discover the most efficient. The trials were not in fact held until 1881 when the Committee recommended

The 'floating gun-carriage'. Armstrong's first iron warship, *Staunch*.

First class battleship *Kashima*, built at Elswick for the Japanese Navy.

the Gardner gun 'as the most suitable 0.45 inch machine gun for introduction into the service'. R. J. Gatling, the president of the company, wrote to Rendel that 'We think it would be a serious mistake if the conclusions of the Committee should be confirmed at the War Office.' He did not think the trials were 'of that exhaustive character which should decide so important a question'. But his views were not to matter much for a new and far superior rival was on the way—the Maxim gun. This was a truly automatic weapon for the weapon's recoil was turned to good account by being the means for inserting a new cartridge. Until this time, the recoil action had been considered a necessary evil. The Maxim, by putting the recoil to good use, was the first really automatic weapon. The Gatling and similar guns were worked by hand in the sense that the barrels were revolved by hand cranking.

In the normal course, one supposes, that Hiram Maxim would have wanted Armstrong to become his British licensee. But Armstrong was, of course, already committed to the Gatling Gun. Maxim looked elsewhere and eventually chose Vickers. From now on, Armstrong found business declining as the Maxim prospered. It was perhaps his most important failure in a normally successful business career of choosing winners.

But in the early days the sales success of the Gatling Gun helped to stimulate still further the development of the Armstrong Works and of the adjacent district. By 1870 the Works, which 20 years before covered five acres of land, stretched for three-quarters of a mile along the river front. The 1851 census gave the population of Elswick as 3,539. By 1871 it had grown to 27,800. This staggering growth rate is a reflection of the expansion of the Works. For as it grew it sucked in workmen from Ireland, Scotland or the countryside. Houses and streets were thrown up in a constant attempt to keep up with the flow of immigrants. What had been a large spread of bare land was quickly covered by row upon row of houses and streets, all climbing precariously up the steep slope that led from the river and the Armstrong works. Scotswood Road, not long ago a rural lane, was now the centre of one of the most concentrated industrial and residential areas in Britain: on the south side, the engineering and armament factory; on the north side, the massed rows of houses interspersed by nothing but shops and ubiquitous public houses. On almost every street corner there was a pub, nearly all of them named after industry—the Crooked Billet, the Vulcan, the Blast Furnace, the Forge Hammer, the Hydraulic Crane, the Gun, the Ordnance Arms, the Rifle. They were well used for they gave one of the few reliefs in a rather depressing life. They were even open before the men went to work. They were allowed to open at six o'clock, five minutes before the work gates were closed. As six o'clock rang out, the pub doors were thrown open, the men streamed in. All along the bars were lines and lines of cups of tea or small nips of rum and whisky. The men instinctively grabbed the drink of their choice, gulped it down and dashed across the road to work.

The early morning ritual at least provided a bright spot in a hard life. Working in an armament factory was tough. Wages were not particularly good. Hours were long, ten hours a day, six days a week. Life expectancy was short. Engineers were dying at an average age of 37, their wives at 36. In such circumstances, it is perhaps surprising that relations between men and masters remained so good for so long. There had been a small dispute, as we have seen, in 1862. For the rest the massive growth of the factory and the residential area had occurred remarkably smoothly. But now in 1871 the most serious labour trouble in Armstrong's long career erupted.

### THE NINE-HOUR MOVEMENT

It was caused by the Nine-Hour Movement, a determined effort to reduce the working day by an hour, thus cutting the number of hours a week from 60 to 54. The campaign had already been waged in Sunderland and had proved a success. The leaders now turned their attention to the Tyne and in particular to Sir W. G. Armstrong and Company. A meeting on Saturday, 22nd April, 1871 resolved that 'the time has arrived when the present excessive hours of labour might, without injury to the employer and with great advantage to the workmen, be reduced to nine hours per day or 54 hours per week'. The meeting also urged that 'it would be far better for the matter to be settled by arbitration'.

Of course. But the employers were not sympathetic. For one

thing they thought the men lacked organization and therefore funds. So they did, at the beginning. But in April they
formed a 'Nine Hours League' which became in effect a trade
union, organizing the campaign and raising and dispensing
strike funds.

By May 1871, the men were ready to send their request to
the engineering employers of Newcastle 'that you kindly
consent to the reduction of our hours of labour from ten to
nine per day—or more properly speaking from 59 hours to
54 hours per week; a concession, we believe, that might be
made with little or no injury to your own interests and with
great advantage to ours ... In conclusion, gentlemen, we
venture to express the hope that you will not utterly ignore
our claims to consideration by treating this with the silence
which looks so like contempt'.

The employers did not treat the request with silence. But
they did something equally maladroit. They instructed a firm
of solicitors 'Stanton and Atkinson' to send their reply in
curt legalese:

'We are instructed by the Manufacturing Engineers to
forward to you the following resolution, viz: "At a meeting
of Associated Employers ... it was unanimously resolved that
the application be declined."'

The men received this reply with 'astonishment and indigna-
tion'. It was 'in the most objectionable form imaginable—
from a firm of solicitors—to the radical workingmen of Newcastle the most obnoxious firm of solicitors that could have
been chosen, the solicitors of the Conservative Association'.

Behind the employers' attitude one can clearly detect the
hand of Armstrong. He was the biggest industrialist in the
city. His prestige was by far the highest. He had been the
main instigator of the Employers Association, of which he was
now the chairman.

The men decided they had no alternative but to strike and
7,500 of them handed in strike notices at 12 factories. About
2,700 struck at Elswick. The employers, led by Armstrong,
resolved 'that united opposition be given to the strike which
has commenced'. Armstrong decided to close his works, a
step that caused anxiety among many who would become
affected, like shopkeepers. Anxiety was to sharpen as the

weeks and then months passed with no sign of a settlement. For the thousands on strike, their only income was 3s. a week strike pay.

Skilled men drained away from Tyneside. John Burnett, the men's leader in the struggle, later wrote: 'Men were being continually sent for by employers in all parts of the country.' Armstrong himself wrote of 'the best old hands ... most of whom have gone away and found work elsewhere'. And the United States Consul in Newcastle wrote: 'The United States acquired some first class workmen in the course of this strike.' In fact within the first three weeks it was estimated that 4,000 men had left the area. By the end of the strike in October up to 6,000 had left.

On the other hand, those who remained received exceptional support, financial as well as moral, from sympathetic colleagues. Altogether, £20,000 was contributed by unionists. The railwaymen gave £50 a week, the Northumberland miners £20 a week and the Durham miners the same. This support was especially noticeable in view of the apathy of the National Executive of the Engineering union, to which most of the striking men belonged. The Webbs in their history of Trade Unionism declared: 'What proved to be the greatest trade union movement since 1852 was undertaken in spite of official disapproval of the governing body and was carried to a successful issue without the provision from headquarters of any leadership or control.'

In August the employers tried to break the strike by opening their works and urging the moderates to return to their employment without penalty. Only a dozen men did so. The employers then tried to import 2,000 engineers from abroad. Over a thousand came from Denmark, Sweden, Belgium and Germany. Their arrival caused a great deal of bitterness. The *Newcastle Weekly Chronicle* commented: '... there has now arisen a bitterness of feeling which bodes no good for the peace and prosperity of the district. It is less a strike than a sort of social war that is raging on Tyneside today.'

Other newspapers were critical of the employers. *The Times* remarked: 'We are inclined to consider the conduct of the employers throughout this dispute as imprudent and impolitic.' *The Spectator*: 'Masters who reply cavalierly by lawyers' letters to the demands of their men, refuse personal discussion and act as nearly as they can like despotic governments against revolutionary bodies can hardly expect their moral claim on the sympathy of the public to be conceded.'

The latter particularly stung Armstrong, who replied: 'We had imagined that a determined effort to wrest concessions from employers by sheer force of combination was not a thing which found favour with the more educated and intelligent classes.'

Armstrong then tried another tactic. He offered a 5% wage increase to all skilled workers. 'Surely,' he wrote, 'they might accept such terms without any sense of defeat.' The men pointed out that since a five per cent wage increase was the equivalent of three hours pay and since the employers had already offered a two-hour reduction, they could surely concede a 54-hour week at the former rates of pay. And so it proved. In October, the employers caved in. 'The sudden manner in which the resistance of the employers collapsed astonished nearly everyone,' wrote John Burnett, the men's leader.

No doubt the explanation was the realization that profits were being lost at a time when rising demand was filling their order books but they were unable to fulfil the work. Whatever the reason, the employers conceded the claim. The nine-hour day was to be introduced from 1st January 1872. Some firms introduced it straight away. The men had scored a great victory. The *Shipping World* commented: 'It is to the Tyneside engineers ... that the skilled workers of the United Kingdom are indebted for establishing the day's work at nine hours.'

The employers were damaged in reputation. Armstrong in particular had displayed not only a tough, unbending attitude but also a poor grasp of tactics. He was no longer the sympathetic employer he had been in his early days, but a rather repressive Tory. Inevitably, his reputation suffered. For his part, the dispute confirmed his decision to leave the day-to-day running of business to his lieutenants while he bent his attention to a new task, the building of a country house and estate. It became the main passion of his declining years.

# CHAPTER SIX

CRAGSIDE

KRUPP and Armstrong were rivals not only in armaments but also in housebuilding. For both of them became passionately involved in the design and erection of a large country mansion. Armstrong said of his country home: 'I could not give the faintest idea of the pleasure it has afforded me ... it has been my very life.' Krupp could have said the same. Like Armstrong, he decided in the 1860's that he needed a mansion to match his style, a house fit for a Cannon King, a house where he could appropriately entertain Royalty. He designed and built Villa Hugel, with 300 bedrooms, over a period of five years. The result was a crazy labyrinth of long corridors, secret quarters and bedrooms with three rows of barriers each to guard them. It was, as it were, a physical manifestation of his own mind—extravagant, devious, suspicious. Armstrong's 'Cragside', built near Rothbury in mid-Northumberland, seemed insignificant by comparison. Yet it, too, in its way represented the characteristics of its owner—straightforward, stylish and country-loving. The creation of 'Cragside' was— and is—a magnificent achievement, a large-scale transformation of a wild, barren part of Northumberland into a romantic area of luscious vegetation. As an official guide described it, here is 'a veritable fairyland of fir-fringed locks, deep and lovely gorges, idyllic walks ... eight miles through a wonderland of beauty.' Another early account recorded: 'Cragside has been described as a romance in stone and mortar. The phrase happily describes one of the strongest impressions the visitor carries away from Cragside but there is something more than romance about the solid, handsome structure, with its extensive and in some respects remarkable demesne—or rather, above and beyond the romance of colour and form, there is the romance of science, of hard struggle with nature, of power and determination overcoming seemingly insuperable difficulties.'

Of course, the investment of large sums of money reduces 'insuperable difficulties' to manageable proportions. Armstrong spared no cost to turn a barren area into an oasis of lushness. In the mid-1860's the valley was unfrequented and the moors solitary apart from the turnpike road to Alnwick. A local naturalist described it then as 'sombre and somewhat lonesome'. Within the vicinity there were only two rather small and tumbling buildings and an old woollen mill. The main feature was a huge crag over three hundred feet high, which was to become the location of the mansion itself.

Why did Armstrong choose such an unpromising spot? He himself said: 'When I resolved to have a country house, I looked to Rothbury, because the district had many old associations for me; I was so much here in my younger days —as a child I was often afflicted with a severe cough and the physician used to order me to Rothbury, where the air proved very beneficial.'

As a little boy he came to Rothbury with his mother, father and sister nearly every year for a holiday. Of those early years he said: 'I was scarcely ever away from the waterside and fished from morning till night ... They used to call me "The Kingfisher".' Sometimes he would follow the example of the locals in doing a little poaching. 'I have many a time crept under the bushes close to the house (Brinkburn Priory) and filled my creel.'

When he began in business, his visits to Rothbury ended for a long time. But then in 1863 when the British Association meeting in Newcastle, over which he presided, came to an end, 'I thought I should like to see the old place once more and, accompanied by two friends, we drove through from Morpeth and stayed over the weekend. The morning after our arrival we walked down by the side of the river beyond the Thrum Mill and scrambled along what is now called the Cragside Hill and sat on a boulder just above where the house now stands. I said to my friends: "What a pretty park that would make if all those hedges were taken away." I little thought then that I should carry out the suggestion ... I thought nothing more about it but on my return to Newcastle a house at Rothbury haunted me so much that I made enquiries about the site with the intention of buying it.'

At first he bought only twenty acres of land from the Duke of Northumberland and built a small house with ten bedrooms. But as the transformation began and the uninteresting land gave way to a 'romantic picture of craggy hills, densely wooded with pines and evergreens' Armstrong's interest was increasingly quickened. He had always been a practical man. Here was a fascinating and abiding practical challenge. He had always been a keen walker and fisherman. Here was an interest that aroused his feelings for nature. He had become somewhat disheartened and depressed by the messy world of commerce. Here was something straightforward.

And so, as he planned and created, built and planted, Cragside grew in his mind's eye. He took over more land. He built more rooms. He planted more trees. By the end, over 1,700 acres belonged to him and he had planted over seven million trees. The villagers of Rothbury, four miles away, detected a noticeable change in the temperature. For the trees helped to cut off the north winds that continually sweep over Northumberland. At the same time, they seemed to make the air even purer, the pine trees in particular filling it with a resinous and health-giving fragrance. But the trees, although numerous, were outdone by plants and bushes. Armstrong took a special delight in azaleas and rhododendrons which he planted in profusion. He also loved lakes and waterfalls. Altogether he turned seventy acres of land over to water in five large lakes, two in the valley and three on the top of the hill to the east of the house.

Elsewhere, he made a principal feature of the streams that ran through the grounds. 'The walk before us now in following the stream cannot be surpassed in the beauty of earth, wood, water and tree on every side,' an early visitor wrote. 'The artificial waterfall, in the construction of which Sir William took an active part, hammer and trowel in hand, and the rustic bridges add greatly to the beauty of the walk and, on reaching the last of these bridges, we hear the constant beat of the hydraulic ram as it sends the water from the adjoining lake to the various parts of the garden and houses ... Sir William himself is the inventor of this wonderful machine, which goes day and night without attendance.'

The enormous transformation of nature complemented the

work done in the mansion. The architect was perhaps the most eminent of his day, Norman Shaw, who was noted for the originality of his ideas and the beautiful detail, indeed richness of his ornamentation. Some critics, however, did not like what he did at Cragside. One complained: 'His work was not altogether free from the somewhat lifeless Gothicism and although Cragside is considered one of the most successful of his earlier country houses, it has not the simplicity and breadth of his later work, nor is there displayed here the refinement of design and masterly handling of material which characterizes the best of modern domestic architecture.' In overall concept, however, the mansion is in keeping with its rocky surroundings. It appears 'craggy' itself, strong and jutting and immovable.

The present-day architectural critic, Nikolaus Pevsner, said: 'What (Shaw) was concerned with was high picturesqueness for his design and he has without doubt achieved it.' The building is full of quaint gables, high-pitched red-tiled roofs, towering, moulded and twisted chimney stacks. There was a gargoyle or two, an elaborate wind-vane and on the west front a castle-like façade. The main impression is one of towering heights everywhere.

While the outside might appear sombre and unappealing, Armstrong made the interior comfortable and pleasant. Many of the walls were fitted with panelled oak. The rooms were invariably large and high-ceilinged. He hung up his valuable collection of paintings: Millais' 'Jeptha' and 'Chill October', a Turner seascape, O'Neil's 'Death of Rafaelle', a cattle picture by Sydney Cooper, Bonheur's 'Forest of Fontainbleu' and many more.

The dining room contained a huge fireplace with cosy inglenooks and large 'fire-dog' irons. An elaborately carved mantelpiece bore the motto: 'East or West, hame's best'. Four stained-glass windows were set into the walls, each representing a season of the year. But this mantelpiece was as nothing to the enormous, highly ornate mantelpiece in the drawing room upstairs. This reached up to the ceiling, twenty feet high, an overwhelming exercise in ostentatious decoration.

Within fourteen years, the work was finished. He had spent innumerable hours planning and superintending. Now in his mid-seventies he could start to enjoy what he had built. So could others. For Cragside became an attraction for thousands of visitors, most of them ordinary people, who were invited to enjoy the gardens, but some of them were people of note. The Shah of Persia came. So did the King of Siam and the representatives of many foreign royal families or governments. But the most notable visitors were the Prince and Princess of Wales and their family, who stayed there in 1884 for three days. A local paper reported: 'The number of country people who flocked into Rothbury to do honour to the royal guests was the largest that has ever been known in the annals of the little country town.' No doubt one of the most interesting features of the house for the royal family was the use of electricity. Cragside was, in fact, the first private residence in the country to have electricity. Joseph Swan, the inventor of the incandescent light, and a close friend of Armstrong, installed it personally in December 1880.

The electricity was derived from water power, thus combining two of Armstrong's principal scientific interests—electricity and water power. Armstrong with several of his employees, including Andrew Richardson who was later to look after the electrical plant, started to dam an ornamental lake in 1879. The purpose was to increase the power of a small brook running out of it. A pipeline was then laid from the brook to a power house that they built. Days of feverish tests followed when a turbine, built at Kendal, was installed in the power house and cables were laid to the hall. The whole enterprise worked perfectly almost from the beginning. At first, the only lamps available were the highly unsuccessful arc lamps. Swan's incandescent lamps solved that problem. The little brook then began to supply the power for 48 lamps in Cragside, the first time the world had known a building lit by electricity derived from water power.

This was not the only interesting feature.

There were two lifts, operated by hydraulic power naturally. There was an hydraulically-controlled spit in the enormous kitchen and the central heating was also operated by an hydraulic engine. The house also contained an electric sewing machine, a laboratory and telescope, telephone communication between rooms and a system of electric gongs. A contemporary account aptly described it as 'truly the palace of a modern magician'.

## PUBLIC BENEFACTIONS

The Prince and Princess of Wales had come north for the formal opening to the public of Jesmond Dene in Newcastle. The land had been given to the City by Armstrong as an extension to the 26 acres of his estate which he had given in 1878. On that occasion the Mayor, Thomas Robinson, had talked of Armstrong's 'munificent gift' and his 'princely liberality in presenting to the town of Newcastle a gift which must enhance inestimably the value and picturesqueness of the proposed Heaton Park and by affording a source of health-giving recreation to the inhabitants, contribute in the highest degree to their social improvement and happiness'. Now in 1884, when Armstrong handed over the whole of Jesmond Dene and the banqueting hall, the Council was almost over-whelmed. One member went so far as to declare: 'If we travelled a thousand miles from this town, I doubt whether we would find grounds where everything thrives and puts on its best vesture as in Jesmond Dene.'

He had by now become noted for his public gifts. As we have seen, he had given the Literary and Philosophical Society, of which he was president, £1,450 for a new lecture hall. In 1859 he had given £600 towards the cost of a new building for the Northern Counties Institution for the Deaf and Dumb. He was one of the chief founders of the Hospital for Sick Children. He gave £2,000 to the Prudhoe Convalescent Home and £500 to the Infirmary for Diseases of the Eye. Especially, he was a true friend of the Royal Victoria Infirmary. In 1870 he gave £2,500 for the building of a new operating theatre, but declined an invitation to the formal opening ceremony. 'I do not see much good to be got from a formal opening of the new operating room' he wrote from Cragside. 'At all events, my presence must be excused, as I have no taste for the kind of speeches that are made on such occasions.' A few years later, he gave £1,000 towards the sum of £2,260 needed for some new wards. In addition, he had provided an annual subscrip-tion of £50 for many years, together with a sum of between

£80 and £100 received from admissions to Jesmond Dene. In 1893 he gave £2,000 from the estate of his wife on her death. But the greatest gift occurred after his own death. His nephew, Mr W. A. Watson-Amstrong, wrote to the Governing Committee in 1901: 'Mrs Watson-Armstrong and I are desirous of raising in Newcastle, the city of his birth, round which during a long life his chief affections centred, a memorial worthy of Lord Armstrong. There was no institution in which he took a keener interest than in the Royal Infirmary ... I have therefore determined to hand over to your committee the sum of one hundred thousand pounds to be used either for the building or endowment of the Infirmary as may seem to them best to meet existing circumstances.' This allowed the building of a new hospital, so long delayed for lack of funds, to go ahead quickly.

During his life, Armstrong also gave numerous sums towards educational or church projects, including £11,500 to the Hancock Natural History Museum. He was a generous subscriber to the funds which established the College of Physical Science, the forerunner of Newcastle University. With the rapid development of engineering in the North East from the mid-century onwards, the need for such a college became increasingly urgent. A campaign was organized in 1853 but it was not until 1871 that it achieved success. In 1874 it was incorporated with the University of Durham, even though its buildings were in Newcastle. Armstrong was a member of the council of the Durham College of Science, as it became known, from 1878 until his death in 1900. He also laid the foundation stone for the new buildings in 1887. After his death, the college took the title of Armstrong College in memory of him.

His greatest act of benevolence was to occur almost at the end of his life. In 1894, he bought Bamburgh Castle, on the wild coast of Northumberland, from the trustees of Lord Crewe, for £60,000. He immediately set about the task of converting it into a convalescent home. In addition, he endowed it with £20,000 towards running costs. Such benevolence was indeed impressive but then he did have the money. When he died he left £2m. in cash in the bank—and that was but a proportion of his wealth.

## THE FUTURE OF COAL

The prosperity and growth of the North East of England had been largely based on a fortune of nature: vast quantities of top-class coal lying beneath its surface. As early as the seventeenth century, this great natural resource was being widely exploited. Great fleets of coal-carrying ships were sailing from the Tyne for Northern France, North West Germany and the Low Countries. But Newcastle's chief markets were London and East Anglia. So powerful was this fleet of colliers and so extensive the numbers employed that the Stuart kings regarded the North East coal trade as the nursery of the Navy.

Over the years the trade grew even greater. In 1844, for example, about two and a half million tons of coal were delivered to the London market, nearly all from Newcastle, Sunderland and Stockton. This tonnage represented almost 9,500 separate sea cargoes and the employment of 10,000 men. By 1863 the annual output of coal from the northern coalfield was estimated at £6,650,000—the value of the business was twice that of the next most important industry, metal manufacture.

The presence of coal led to many other developments. It stimulated the growth of shipbuilding, particularly the colliers to carry the coal. One yard, Palmers of Hebburn on Tyne, turned out so many colliers that the local joke was that it produced them by the mile and cut them off to the required length! It led, too, to the development of iron and steel making, which was stimulated further by the growing demand for iron for both railways and ships and also by the discovery of local ores. The biggest and best deposits in the country were found in the Cleveland hills in North Yorkshire. The discovery was responsible for the growth of Middlesbrough. Between 1851 and 1861, the town's population increased by 137 per cent and went on rising at a very fast rate for the rest of the century. Slightly further north, the Consett Iron Works in County Durham were established in 1841 originally to work local ores but within a few years they were supplied from Cleveland. 'What had once been a barren moor without population for miles around speedily became an immense hive of industry,' one historian wrote.[1] Four years later, Henry

Bolckow and Henry Vaughan started the Witton Park Iron Works near Bishop Auckland in County Durham and in the same year the Weardale Iron and Coal Company began operations at Stanhope.

Coal thus played an absolutely fundamental part in the economy of the region. But already one or two people were beginning to see the dangers ahead. One of them was Armstrong. In his presidential address to the British Association for the Advancement of Science meeting in Newcastle in 1863, he took this problem as his main theme. He said: 'The greatness of England much depends upon the superiority of her coal in cheapness and quality over that of other nations; but we have already drawn from our choicest mines a far larger quantity of coal than has been raised in all the other parts of the world put together and the time is not remote when we shall have to encounter the disadvantages of increased cost of working and diminished value of produce.'[2]

He then considered estimates of how long the British coal supply would last. In 1861, Armstrong pointed out, the 'enormous total' of eighty-six million tons of coal had been mined, three times as much as twenty years previously. He calculated that there were 80,000 million tons of coal lying beneath the surface and that '200 years will be sufficient to exhaust the principal seams even at the present rate of working ... Were we reaping the full advantage of all the coal we burnt, no objection could be made to the largeness of the quantity but we are using it wastefully and extravagantly in all its applications.' In particular, he thought that steam engines were very inefficient users of coal. He calculated that in doing a given amount of work with a steam engine only one-thirtieth of the energy of the coal was being used. Equally, factory and domestic fires allowed too much useful energy to escape. 'The combustion in common furnaces is so imperfect that clouds of powdered carbon, in the form of smoke, envelope our manufacturing towns, and gases which ought to be completely oxygenized in the fire pass into the air with two-thirds of their heating power undeveloped.'

The particular aspect of smoke was one on which he could speak with first-hand authority. For in 1857 and 1858 he had carried out a series of experiments, with two other engineers, to test the possibility of preventing smoke in the burning of coal in steam-engine boilers. The experiments, costing £500, had been paid for by the Northumberland Steam Collieries Association. The northern coal owners were primarily interested in saving their market from stiff competition from the South Wales coalfield. The Admiralty had objected to the continuing use of north-country coal which, it claimed, was so smoky, it 'acted as a signal to an enemy of the approach of a hostile squadron'. The Welsh coal was more expensive but produced less smoke and more heat. The Government decided to switch from Northumberland to Welsh coal.

Naturally alarmed, the north-country coal owners commissioned Armstrong, James Longridge, an engineer, and Thomas Richardson, professor of chemistry at Durham University, to carry out experiments to reduce the output of smoke. They spent two years on the project. The results of their research showed not only how smoke could be reduced but that, contrary to what had been stated by the Admiralty, north-country coal had greater heating power than coal from Wales.

Armstrong declared: 'I can state with perfect confidence that, so far as the raising of steam is concerned, the production of smoke is unnecessary and inexcusable. The experiments proved beyond a doubt that, by an easy method of firing, combined with a due admission of air and a proper arrangement of fire-grate, not involving any complexity, the emission of smoke might be perfectly avoided.' As a result of the research, the Admiralty had to drop its objections to Northumberland coal.

But there was the wider, more fundamental problem of the exhaustion of the coal supplies, which Armstrong had made the central theme of his British Association address. His anxiety was so clear and his position so eminent, the Government felt obliged to act. It took the standard course of setting up a royal commission to enquire into the problem. It sat in 1866 with Armstrong himself as both a member and one of the chief witnesses.

Armstrong was to return to the subject twice more in public speeches. One occasion was his presidential address to the North of England Institute of Mining and Mechanical

Engineers in 1873 and the other his presidential address to the mechanical section of the British Association meeting at York in 1883. At York he discussed the possibility of preventing the 'monstrous waste' of the steam engine by using electrical methods to obtain power. In 1863 he had felt that 'whether we use heat or electricity as the motive power, we must equally depend upon chemical affinity as the source of supply ... But where are we to obtain materials so economical for this purpose as the coal we derive from the earth and the oxygen we obtain from the air?'[2] But by 1883 the advances made by electrical science suggested to him that a thermo-electric engine might 'not only be used as an auxiliary but in complete substitution for the steam engine because it might be used to activate 'the direct heating action of the sun's rays'. He estimated that 'the solar heat, operating upon an area of one acre in the tropics, would, if fully utilised, exert the amazing power of 4,000 horses acting for nearly nine hours every day'. He could foresee that 'whenever the time comes for utilising the power of great waterfalls, the transmission of power by electricity will become a system of vast importance'. This prophecy, like so much else of what he said on this subject, was soon to materialize in schemes at Geneva and Niagara. Hydro-electric schemes are now, of course, commonplace. But the more efficient use of coal and the reduction of the smoke problem, on which he spoke with such anxiety a hundred years ago, have still to be achieved.

### A VISIT TO EGYPT

Armstrong disliked travel. Only once did he go outside Europe—in January and February 1872 when he visited Egypt with a friend. 'It was like entering upon a new life to be suddenly brought in contact with camels and turbans and palm-trees and dark-skinned men, clothed in many-coloured garments,' he recorded.[3]

Yet even on a trip like this to a country which must have had an overpowering climate for a man now into his sixties, his old instincts and habits remained with him. You might have thought he would want to take things easy, to stroll lazily through the day, to find some recompense for all those

One of the heavy gun machine shops showing 8in., 9in., and 12in. guns under manufacture.

Sir Andrew Noble.

years when he had forsaken a holiday. Not so. He was almost as busy as he would have been in his office or laboratory. Altogether he travelled over three thousand miles, going deep down into the Sudan. He observed. He inspected. He investigated. He researched. Egyptian hieroglyphics interested him and he became something of an authority. He studied the temples and pyramids. He explored the rocks and ancient tombs. Wherever he went or whoever he saw, he was curious, asking questions, wanting information. In effect, he was the typical scientist on holiday, finding his enjoyment from the habits and techniques normally employed so diligently in his work. When he got back, his trip provided a fascinating story for the members of the Literary and Philosophical Society. He entertained them to four lectures, each lasting over two hours. On every occasion, he played to a packed house.

He travelled overland by way of Paris, Turin, Rome, Naples, Brindisi and then crossing to Alexandria. This journey in itself must have been taxing for a man of sixty-two, although hardly a word of complaint is contained in his story. The nearest he comes to giving a picture of the physical effect upon him is in talking of the climate in the Sudan, or Nubia. 'It was the month of February when we were in Nubia and the weather was that of a splendid summer—hot, but so dry as not to be oppressive ... I should say the winter climate of Nubia is much superior for invalids to that of Egypt, for though the mid-day sun is hotter, the nights and mornings are much milder and thus the changes of temperature so trying to invalids are avoided.'

The visit to Egypt began at Alexandria, a town he did not like. 'Alexandria possesses none of its ancient grandeur. It is essentially a seafaring place, reminding one, in many respects, of Wapping; and one looks in vain for any remnants of that love of philosophy and literature for which it used to be so famous.'

In Cairo, he was in for another surprise—of a completely different kind. 'All the chambermaids were of the masculine gender; that is to say, they were bare-legged Arab men who performed the duties of chambermaids in a quiet and efficient manner.' He was also much struck by the appearance of the general public, at least as he observed them from his window in Shepherd's Hotel. 'There was every graduation in appearance between extreme dignity and extreme grotesqueness, and not unfrequently these two qualities were combined.'

His first problem was knowing what to wear, or rather how much. He noticed some were wearing 'almost nothing at all'; others 'such a reduplication of garments as would oppress an Englishman, even in his own climate'. He tried both systems and in the end favoured the latter for 'little was gained in coolness, under a scorching sun, by reducing the thickness of clothing while the risk of chill in the shade and at sunset was very seriously increased.'

After seeing the modern Cairo, he plunged into the historic sector. He found it picturesque. 'There are no sewers and the streets are never swept but the dogs and cats act as scavengers and the sun dries up the residue.' He also came upon the habit of slavery. 'There is scarcely a house in Cairo without one or more slaves; but in general they are kindly treated, moderately worked and become much attached to the family in which they are placed.' No words of condemnation therefore, although he did say : 'The manner in which the poor creatures are kidnapped is atrocious and is by far the worst part of the business. There are gangs of ruffians on the White Nile who do this horrible work and their mode of proceeding is to make incursions into adjacent lands and there, surrounding the villages, they set fire to everything that will burn. When the people rush out of their houses, the men are shot down, the children captured and the women left to starve or provide for themselves. This villainous pursuit is not, however, without danger; for, sometimes, the villagers get information of what is coming and then, by combining amongst themselves, they overpower their enemies and slaughter them without mercy.' From Cairo, he travelled south, visiting the Pyramids, most of which he found in 'a state of complete ruin'. Then on to Memphis—'It takes one's breath away to think of the antiquity of Memphis'—to Siout—'Nothing can exceed the luxuriance of the land round Siout'—and down as far as Nubia—'In picturesque effect it is infinitely superior to Egypt.' Even here despite the overwhelming heat, Armstrong's diligent surveying and enquiring went on. And all of this, all this long and exhausting journey, was packed into a few weeks.

Even the return home was undertaken rapidly, so rapidly that he arrived home to snow and fog.

## ARMSTRONG IN LATER LIFE

His years of enormous fame and success seemed to bring little or no change to Armstrong's personality. Throughout his life, he seemed to be quiet, reflective, serious and responsible. Above all others, perhaps the word 'respectable' best sums him up. He neither smoked nor drank, except in the strictest moderation. He had no affairs of the heart. He abhored the 'vulgar practice of swearing'. Any task he tackled was completed with conscientious thoroughness, whether it was a scientific project, the construction of Cragside or the development of the factory itself.

A close friend, John Worsnop of Rothbury, said of him: 'What struck one most about Lord Armstrong was his marvellous energy and love of work. Work was absolutely necessary to him and whatever the work might be, great or small, he entered into it with all his heart and soul.'[4]

He is described by a number of his friends as genial yet no smile, however slight, plays about his lips in the many portraits done of him. No anecdotes displaying a lighter side to his nature are handed down. The present Lord Armstrong, who recalls his famous predecessor with clarity, never heard him say an amusing thing. But he does remember that each day Lord Armstrong would send for him and give him a short lecture on electricity, followed by an acid drop out of a big bottle. One day, the little boy, aged then about four, dared to ask for another one but the request met with a stern frown.

Yet Armstrong, who had no children of his own, had a strong liking for them. He liked to have them around him for a little part of each day. In winter he would skate on the Cragside lakes with the local boys. At first, they were somewhat in awe of him but when they saw how natural he was, they enjoyed his company. He seems to have been without pretence. Another friend said he was 'destitute of pride and unaffectedly simple in manner'. Such a characteristic would explain his ease with children.

He was a good-looking man, perhaps to some even handsome, with a strong face and even features. His hair receded in the middle but he made up for such a shortage by the Victorian habit of cultivating powerful side whiskers. He was tallish and rather wiry—in fact in later life his clothes seemed to hang on him in a limp fashion as if he had not enough flesh to fill them out. Although neat, clothes did not interest him.

Perhaps little did, apart from his work. This absorbed him almost entirely. Whether the problem was scientific or commercial or practical (as in the building of Cragside) he gave it his single-minded attention. Nothing distracted him. Almost to the end of his life he was able to concentrate powerfully upon the given subject. Worsnop said: 'He could think so deeply as to render himself perfectly oblivious to his surroundings.'

For this reason his life was divided clearly into three main sections: the creation of the engineering works; the development of armaments; the building of Cragside. There is no overlap—each is a distinctly separate phase. His earlier life when he had to combine his legal profession and his engineering interests was so frustrating for him, mainly for this reason.

He found relaxation in country sports, particularly walking and fishing. In fact, he gained the nickname 'Kingfisher' because of his prowess with the rod. When he was in his eighties, he went fishing in one of the lakes at Cragside and achieved the unusual distinction of catching two fish with one cast—an achievement of which he was almost childishly proud. The household talked about it for months to come.[4] The arts interested him only in a conventional way. He bought paintings as investments rather than for the pleasure they brought. He did not go to the theatre often and musical evenings at home were rare. What he liked, above all, was to talk with friends about scientific matters or increasingly as he grew older about politics. He had been an instinctive Liberal in his younger days without giving politics much time or thought. As he grew older, he became more interested and more Right Wing. Partly this was due to the Nine-Hour Movement and the growing strength of the unions, a tendency he deplored. But it was the question of Irish Home Rule that really ignited his political interest. He was absolutely opposed to Gladstone's policy and after his elevation to the Peerage in 1887, he attended all the debates in the House of Lords on the subject, always speaking as an implacable opponent of such a policy.

His marriage seems to have been a happy one, although perhaps a little dull. Margaret, his wife, was dutiful in the Victorian manner, acting as the hostess when her husband entertained, running the household efficiently, taking a keen, practical interest in the garden and doing good works. Yet one cannot help wondering whether she was happy. She had been born into a comfortable middle-class home in Bishop Auckland in County Durham, where her father had a small engineering business. She and Armstrong had been childhood sweethearts and as far as we know, he never even considered another girl for his wife. They were married when they were in their mid-twenties. Then she disappears. Scarcely a record, scarcely indeed a word occurs about her. For years Armstrong is totally occupied developing first the engineering, then the armament business. Then when he is famous, there are so many people to meet and to entertain. Did she not find it a strain, conversing with kings and princes, with businessmen and scientists, whose talk she can scarcely have understood?

In an alcove of the Picture Gallery at Cragside, there is a glass case containing a heavy, ornate book recording the royal visit to Cragside in 1884. The book contains many delightful paintings of the occasion by a local artist, F. H. Emmerson. But, almost at the end, one is brought up to a halt. Here is a picture of Margaret with an expression of inner-felt sadness under a resolute gaze. And one asks oneself again—was she happy? She had no children. She had a husband who although upright and dutiful was in some ways a stranger from her. She had continually to act a part.

Perhaps this central vacuum made her the domineering woman she became. The servants were frightened of her, indeed often detested her. Some, who were brought up by her because they were orphans and later became servants, told the present Lord Armstrong how much they disliked her. She treated them like pieces of machinery, keeping them busy continuously to prevent their falling into mischief. The maids nearly always found they had a great deal of sewing to do in the evenings. She could also be very abrupt. On one occasion a visitor was sent off to one of the top lakes to do some fishing. By mistake, he fished in one of the lower lakes and caught Lady Armstrong's pet carp. When he came back to the house proudly bearing his catch, she was very short with him. But her stern attitude was combined with a genuine interest in good works. The two characteristics, of course, not infrequently go together.

# CHAPTER SEVEN

## CHANGES IN NAVAL ARTILLERY

FROM about 1870 onwards, the changes that had occurred in land-based artillery were to be adopted for naval purposes. Indeed, the traditional view that Britain's defence started in the Channel now became an overt and definite policy. 'Britannia Rules the Waves' was not simply a motto or a music-hall song. It expressed succinctly the new emphasis in defence policy. But such a policy was made possible only with vast improvements in naval artillery to match the advances being made by other countries, particularly France. For the revolution that had occurred in land-based armaments had had no impact on the navy and the same story of conservatism and prejudice was now to be enacted in the Admiralty as it had been in the War Office.

Public opinion, even expert opinion, was slow to realize that the Battle of Trafalgar fought in 1805 represented the last of the traditional-style of naval battles based on tactical manoeuvring at close quarters. Perhaps there was a good excuse for conservatism for no major sea-battle had been fought since Trafalgar. Of course, there had been some minor engagements, in Algiers in 1816, at Navarino Bay in 1827 and during the Crimean War, but none of them was sufficiently important or decisive to provide evidence of change, or, more important, of the need for it.

What change there had been was towards providing ships with armour-cladding as a superior means of defence. The Admiralty felt that better defence material would negate any improvements in offensive methods by an enemy. The Committee on Designs reporting in 1871 declared: 'We cannot lose sight of the indisputable fact that in an action between an armour-clad and an unarmoured ship (assuming that they carry guns of equal power) the former has and must have, an immense advantage in being able to penetrate the sides of her adversary at a distance at which she herself is impenetrable.' The Committee did not say so but it clearly assumed that the speed of the two ships was equal, too. The assumptions were hardly tenable. Armstrong wrote to Lord Dufferin, the chairman of the Committee: 'At present it is only the most recent of our armour-clads that have any pretence to be considered invulnerable. All the earlier vessels, when built, had just as much claim to be so regarded as the strongest ships of the present day; yet they are now completely left behind and are, in my opinion, much inferior to well-constructed unarmoured ships ... Every addition to the weight carried for defence must be attended with a diminution of armament and of speed, unless the size of the ship be increased in a very rapid proportion.'[1] Although the Committee did not immediately accept Armstrong's view, the day of the big naval gun was drawing very near, thanks largely to Armstrong's work. He believed wholeheartedly that attack was the best form of defence and that the best means of attack was the gun.

There had been no radical improvements in the gun as an important weapon in sea battles for about three centuries. The standard piece of equipment was still the old cast-iron, smooth-bore gun, using a solid ball of iron loaded through the muzzle. It was cumbersome, unreliable, and needed a large number of men. Above all, it was hopelessly inaccurate. Being a round shot and muzzle-loaded, it was anything but a neat fit in the barrel. The ball indeed bounced from one side of the barrel to the other as it was fired and pure chance dictated its final direction. Yet the disadvantages of such inaccuracy were not felt seriously because traditionally guns were not fired until the ships were so close to the enemy that the shot could not possibly miss. In other words, no one considered there was a need for an accurate gun which could hit its target from a long distance.

The traditionalists used two main—and now familiar—arguments. On the one hand, they argued that the smooth-bore gun had worked well for many decades and therefore there was no need to change. On the other hand, they pointed out that thousands of the conventional guns were in existence. It would be financial folly to scrap them. Another argument presented itself with the first of the new projectiles. This was a hollow shell, filled with some form of explosive. Being fired from a smooth-bore gun, it was no more accurate than the old cast-iron ball but it added disadvantages and dangers of its own. For its splinter-like impact would cause painful death to an incalculable number of opponents. At a time when war was still conducted according to gentlemanly rules, this was a strong argument. However, the Russian massacre of the Turkish fleet in the harbour of Sinope in 1853 was directly attributable to the use of the new 'murderous' shells. The world had to take notice.

The action of the shell was one aspect. More important was the question of its accuracy. This could never be improved without changing its shape from a round ball to an elongated projectile and without substituting rifling for the smooth bore of the barrel. These truths had been amply demonstrated by Armstrong, Whitworth and others on land. Now, towards the end of the 1860's the Admiralty was at last ready to listen.

## ARMSTRONG'S FIRST WARSHIPS

As we have seen, Armstrong negotiated a formal arrangement for warship building with Dr Charles Mitchell's Walker shipyard in 1867. Under the agreement, Mitchell would build the ships and Armstrong would arm them. The first ship, H.M.S. *Staunch*, was completed by 1868. Over the next fifteen years about twenty similar vessels were built. They included eleven for the Chinese Navy, two for the Dutch Government and the remaining seven for British or Colonial Governments. They were fitted with muzzle-loading guns 12 inches in diameter and 38 tons in weight jutting over the prow. The greatest displacement was 550 tons and the highest speed 12 knots.

The formal link with Mitchells against a background of increasing interest in warships, stimulated Armstrong to take up naval architecture. He had, of course, for some years investigated the problems of mounting and working guns on ships. He had taken definite sides in the controversy of guns against armour. He believed that no matter what improvements were made in armour—and he had made some himself

by producing steel of high tensile strength and great tough-
ness through tempering it in an oil bath—it would always
be possible for guns to prove victorious. But he felt that what
was needed was a new design, a new type of ship. It needed
to carry effective fire power yet at the same time to move at
speed. His answer was the fast protected cruiser. The first
example was the *Esmeralda* built for the Chilean Government
in 1882.

Armstrong said: 'The *Esmeralda* is the swiftest and most
powerfully-armed cruiser in the world ... She is unarmoured,
as all cruisers ought to be, but as her boilers, engines and
magazines are all below water-level and are covered by a
strong steel water-tight deck, which is also below water-level,
she is almost absolutely secure against the worst effects of
projectiles ... Happily she has passed into the hands of a
nation which is never likely to be at war with England for
I can conceive no more terrible scourge on our commerce than
she would be in the hands of an enemy. No cruiser in the
British navy is swift enough to catch her or strong enough to
take her.'

The *Esmeralda* had a displacement of 2,974 tons yet could
still achieve a speed of 18.25 knots. She was fitted with two
ten-inch breech-loading guns and six 6-inch guns. Although
she was built for the Chilean Government she was later sold
to Japan and renamed *Idzumi*. She was the first vessel of the
Japanese Navy to sight the Russian fleet entering the straits
of Tsushima before the great naval battle between the Russian
and Japanese fleets in 1905. This was a battle that was followed as closely in shipyard drawing offices in England as in
the Imperial Palaces of the belligerent nations. For many of
the vessels had been built in England, especially on the Tyne.
Armstrong had built eight warships for Japan by this time,
including the battleships *Yashima* and *Hatsuse*. On the other
bank of the river Tyne, Hawthorn Leslie had built eight
cruisers for the Russian Volunteer Fleet while another local
shipyard, Swan and Hunter, had built three cruisers for
Russia.

There was naturally great jubilation at Elswick when their
large, swift warships armed with long-range guns of such
striking power won the day so easily. The victory was seen

as a triumph for the work of Armstrong and the head of the shipbuilding department, William White, and his successor Philip Watts all those years earlier. White had been brought in as Warship Designer and Manager of the naval shipyard in 1883. Before that he was Chief Constructor at the Admiralty. The high regard in which Armstrong held him can be judged from the salary he offered of £2,000 a year. The Admiralty had been paying him £600.

White was a friendly man, full of good talk and with a keen sense of humour yet he never really managed to settle down on Tyneside. His wife recalled: 'Although the work he was able to carry out on the Tyne was in every way successful and he had a free hand to develop and execute many of his own ideas in ship construction, he was never quite happy in his north-country work; the harshness of the climate, the rough speech of the men, the black dirt and coaly mud of the Tyneside roads, were uncongenial. He made friends, devoted friends, there as he did everywhere he went; Lord and Lady Armstrong remained his friends all their lives; but he never felt quite at home.'

Within two years he was to return to London and the Admiralty, for the latter, realizing what an excellent man they had lost, adopted the highly unusual course of asking him to return and at a higher salary. The First Lord of the Admiralty, Lord George Hamilton, made the initiative himself. He wrote: 'To bring a public servant back into the Service as head of a department over those who had remained was an unusual procedure, and sure to lead to protest. If it had to be done, it must be done quickly and irrevocably.' Hamilton sent his Permanent Secretary to see White. 'White was most reasonable and stated the terms upon which he was willing to return to the Admiralty, provided Lord Armstrong would allow him to go ... I then wrote to Armstrong, who by return of post most patriotically gave up White ... Both White and Armstrong behaved with patriotism and promptitude. White gave up a large income, and Armstrong surrendered a man whom he knew to be one of the best naval architects of his time.'2

White had made a large technical contribution yet the concept of the cruiser was to a large extent Armstrong's. He had taken a personal interest in the development of the design. He had strongly advocated the building of a large number of vessels of this class of moderate size. For he felt that they would provide the best possible protection for commerce while two or three of them acting together might even be more than a match for an ironclad battleship. Their main features, he thought, were their 'great speed and nimbleness of movement, combined with great offensive power ... little or no side armour, but otherwise constructed to minimize the effects of projectiles.' With the introduction later of high explosives Armstrong adapted his view recommending that even high speed cruisers needed to sacrifice some of their knots to greater safety through the use of side armour.

The cruiser became the new fashion after the usual period of official opposition. Armstrong declared: 'It is surprising that so much apathy should be displayed regarding the unprotected state of our commerce. There is at present a well-founded scare about the insufficiency of our navy but the cry is chiefly for more ironclads which are of little or no use for the protection of commerce, and we hear but little of the need of fast cruisers to save us from depredations at sea. Nothing can be more certain than that in the event of war our merchant shipping would be attacked; and if an enemy contented himself by assailing our commerce with a fleet of swift and powerful steamers, he would give the go-by to our ironclads and inflict fatal injury upon us, with little cost to himself.' His argument soon had effect.

Armstrong's new concept caught on very quickly and orders began to flow in rapidly. To meet them, Armstrong felt he should now open his own yard at Elswick while still continuing the association with Mitchell. This he now set out to do. Fortunately, two serious handicaps, which only a few years before would have negated the scheme, had already been removed. One was the dredging of the river. The other was the replacement of the old Tyne Bridge by a new swing bridge.

Until well into the 1860's the Tyne was largely an undredged river. As late as 1849 an Admiralty enquiry recorded that the average depth of the river at the Bar was only six feet. Most ships had to complete their loading at North Shields, near the river mouth, even though Newcastle, nine miles in-

land, was their depot. One account of those days reported:
'A trip down the river was an enterprise full of eventualities
in the 'forties and 'fifties, not to be hazarded by persons of
weak nerves or temperament and least of all by those who
had been so thoughtless as to come on board without pro-
visions, for to descend to a sporting phrase, it was a five to
one chance that they were not the victims of hunger before
they reached their destination.'[3] There were no docks and few
quays. Nor were there any piers at Shields and gales would
blow tides up on to the beaches. After one bad storm thirty
stranded hulls were counted along the banks of the river.
'The Tyne was a notoriously dangerous port to which the
prudent seaman always gave a wide berth in bad weather or
if he had the temerity to essay an entrance he was often glad
to save his ship by running her high and dry on the south
sands.' Opposite the Elswick works was a large island. Horse
races and athletic sports of all kinds were staged there until
the 1870's while the 'Countess of Coventry' inn was a well-
known landmark. In 1850 the Tyne Improvement Act allowed
a start to be made on turning the river into a proper industrial
channel but it was well into the 'sixties before any noticeable
improvements appeared. Indeed, it was the end of the 1870's
before the river was properly dredged in front of Elswick and
the large island was removed. The river could then flow past
the works in a broad current and Armstrong could think of
opening his own shipyard for ships drawing up to twenty-five
feet of water could come under the sheer-legs.

The second difficulty that had been removed was the old
bridge. This was the third bridge to have been built on that
spot. Completed in 1781, it had nine arches but no houses,
unlike its predecessor which had been destroyed by a flood.
By the mid-nineteenth century, the bridge was proving a
serious handicap to the development of the river. In 1860 Mr
John Ure, Chief Engineer to the Tyne Commissioners, declared: 'As a structure the Town Bridge of Newcastle acts like
a weir ... Its removal is therefore desirable, irrespective of
its acting as a bar to the passage of masted vessels. I propose
therefore to construct a new Low Level Bridge in lieu of the
existing Town Bridge on a plan that would enable the two
centre spans to be opened for the passage of masted vessels.'

His proposal was accepted by the Commissioners ... The stone bridge was removed between 1866 and 1873, all traffic and pedestrians using the High Level Bridge in the interval. Armstrong was commissioned to design and construct the new swing bridge which was opened in 1876. The swing portion was first used on 17th July 1876 when the *Europa* of the Italian Navy passed up to the Elswick Ordnance Works to take on board a 100-ton gun. The gun was hoisted on board by a pair of one hundred and twenty ton hydraulic sheer-legs. When the *Europa* arrived at Spezia, the gun was lifted out by a one hundred and eighty ton hydraulic revolving crane. At that time, in 1876, the gun, the Swing Bridge, the sheer-legs and the hydraulic crane were each the largest of their type in the world and each of them had been made at Elswick.

The new bridge and the deepened river spurred industrial activity. A contemporary report enthused : 'Everywhere, from the dancing waters of the harbour to the ebb and flow of the throbbing city, industry, resource and expansion, coal staiths, shipyards, engine shops, dry docks, chemical works, forges, electric lighting laboratories, warehouses, merchants' offices, steamships, railway trains, without end, without number— from Shields to Scotswood, there is not its like in 13 miles of river the world over. Smoke-ridden, grimy, noisy as it all is, what is it but the free expression of nineteenth-century energy, the epitome of modern industrialism, the thumb-mark of toil, by which the human race is destined to work out its salvation?'[4]

That 'free expression of nineteenth-century energy' was now to be illustrated by Armstrong's opening his own shipyard, concentrating entirely on warships. The Walker yard was to be left free for merchant ship production. Elswick could now produce the complete warship. Its iron and steel works supplied the material; its shipbuilding works produced the vessels; its ordnance department built and fitted the guns. 'The result is that Elswick is now a complete arsenal and can enter into a contract to build, engine, arm and equip a ship of war ready for sea, the whole work, from the keel to providing the finished ship with ammunition, being done on the Tyne.' And another observer commented : 'The Elswick establishment (with its armament manufacture as well as shipbuilding) could be regarded as nothing less than an arsenal which in time of war would be invaluable to this country.'

An enormous and terrifying output now began. In October 1884 the new Elswick yard was inaugurated with the laying-down of the fast protected cruiser *Panther* for the Austro-Hungarian Government. Soon afterwards came the sister ship *Leopard* for the same navy. In the following year, a similar vessel the *Dogali* was built for the Italian Government. More important, Elswick's first battleship, the *Victoria* was laid down together with her sister ship the *Sans Pareil*, the only ships at that time to carry guns of 110-tons. The ships took three years to build. Despite the river dredging and the swing bridge, they were extremely difficult to navigate out to the sea. But the sheer difficulties themselves added to the lustre of their achievement. One can still imagine now the mixture of pride and awe with which they must have been observed by the public crowding the quayside. Not only the size of the vessels but also the ferocity of their armaments must have been an intimidating sight, as they eased past the dear land-marks of the city.

There then took to the water a multitude of men o'war, ships of terrifying proportions for many countries. There were the cruisers *Chih Yuan* and *Ching Yuan* for China, *Isla de Luzon* and *Isla de Cuba* for Spain; the *Elizabeta* for Roumania and the *25 de Mayo* for Argentine. There were also the *Buenos Aires* for the Argentine, at a cost of £383,000, the *Eidsvold* and *Norge* for Norway at a cost of £350,000 each and the *Albany* for America at a cost of £247,600. There were war-ships, too, for Chile and Portugal, Turkey and Brazil. In its thirty years of existence, the Elswick yard produced eighty-four warships—a great navy in itself by any standards.

Many of these ships were the greatest of their time. The British battleships *Victoria* and *Sans Pareil* started in 1885 were the only ships then to carry 110-ton guns. The Italian cruiser *Piemonte*, launched in 1889, was fitted with triple expansion, four cylinder vertical engines giving a speed of 22 knots—in excess of any similar vessel up to that date. And the Japanese battleship *Yashima* laid down in 1894, could produce 20 knots even though she had a displacement of 12,000 tons. She was a battleship with the speed of a cruiser and the firepower of a fortress. She had four 12-inch breach-loading guns, ten six-inch guns and many small ones.

Armstrong himself used a very interesting analogy to dramatize the developments that had been made in naval building. He would compare the Victoria, Elswick's first battle-ship, with Nelson's flagship, the Victory. The heaviest gun on board the Victory, he said, was a little over three tons, the heaviest on board the Victoria was a little over 110 tons. The heaviest shot used in the Victory was 68 lbs.; in the Victoria it was 1,800 lbs. The broadside fire from the Victory consumed only 355 lbs. of powder, that from the Victoria consumed 3,120 lbs. 'These figures show in the most marked manner the enormous advances that have been made in the construction and armament of these marine monsters,' he said, at the launch of the Victoria in April 1887.

But perhaps even more dazzling was the power and extent of the machinery on board the Victoria. She was fitted with no less than twenty-four auxiliary steam engines in connection with her main engines, with thirty steam engines unconnected with her propelling engines and another thirty-two hydraulic engines for various purposes. About 25 years later the firm was building battleships with three times the displacement of the Victoria and building them in only two-thirds of the time. There was one area where the Victory had the advantage. Her total cost was about £100,000—the Victoria cost ten times that much.

Towards the end of the century, Japan was a particularly valuable customer. The Elswick yard designed and built thirteen warships for Japan between 1884 and 1914. They consisted of three battleships and ten cruisers. The early ones were all engaged in the war against Russia in 1905—indeed every single Japanese vessel in that battle was armed with guns supplied by Armstrong.

THE OIL TANKER

Armstrong's firm also pioneered another very important type of vessel, the oil tanker. Today oil tankers are the most important of all the different types of ships being built throughout the world. In fact in 1968 the total world output

George Cruddas.

Sir Joseph Whitworth.

of oil tankers was 6,612,000 tons. But the correct design for these vessels took some time to emerge: indeed more than twenty years passed between the opening of the international trade in oil in 1860 and the discovery of a satisfactory way of transporting the liquid in bulk. At first, all sorts of terrible accidents occurred because shipbuilders failed to appreciate the chemical properties of petrol and a number of the would-be prototypes of the oil tanker blew up.

When oil was discovered in the Baltic in the early 1880's the quest for an effective means of transport was given a new and much more urgent impetus. A Newcastle businessman, Mr Charles Marvin, played a part. He visited the Baltic at about this time and upon his return described his experiences in a local newspaper. This series stirred the enthusiasm of a local shipowner, James McNabb. At about the same time, an Austrian called Singer, a partner in an oil refining business, came to Newcastle in order to find shipowners who would be willing to transport oil around the Baltic. Singer met a number of local shipowners including McNabb. The latter showed himself very interested and he talked to Singer at great length. They discussed the character, the chemical properties and the commercial value of oil. Above all, McNabb learned of the vital need to devise means for drawing off and dispersing the evolved gases from the tanks of the steamer. Using this information, McNabb sketched a plan for an oil tanker and gave a local shipbuilding firm, R. & W. Hawthorn, Leslie and Company, the contract to convert the *Marquis Scicluna* into a bulk carrier. The design conceived dividing the vessel from fore to aft by a bulkhead. Each side was then further divided by four transverse bulkheads. Each of the eight tanks was capable of carrying 250 tons of oil and was covered by an oil-tight platform stretching the full length of the ship. A shaft tunnel ran into each tank for loading and discharging and was completely covered by an outside casing so as to leave a space between it and the tunnel casing. This space would allow the accumulation of gases from the oil which were released to the open air through special escape holes. The conversion work proved successful and the converted vessel began running under her contract in September 1886.

The articles by Marvin in the local paper, the visit by

Singer and the conversion work carried out by McNabb stimulated still further an interest already shown in the subject by Henry F. Swan, a director of Armstrong, Mitchell and Co. Ltd., and managing director of their Low Walker yard. He redoubled his efforts on an alternative system which was to provide the final answer. His basic concept was to use the hull as the receptacle, instead of building tanks inside the hull. His design was simpler and cheaper, reduced waste space and gave greater stability. He took out his first patent in November 1885 and almost immediately implemented the design in the *Gluckauf* built for M. Heinrich Riedemann of Bremen. Swan's patent followed McNabb's design in dividing the vessel from fore to aft by a longitudinal bulkhead and sideways by traverse bulkheads. It was also similar in the use of special expansion trunkways for the accumulation and escape of gases. But it was the design of these trunkways that was the distinguishing feature of Swan's designs. Equally characteristic and of almost equal importance was the use of the shell plating of the vessel to provide the bottom and outer sides of the tanks while the top was formed by a platform, or lower deck. Such a concept meant that more than ever the rivetting and all other joints had to be perfectly tight. An expert commented at the time: 'We know that petroleum will find its way through almost any joint and it requires a shipbuilder to be very clever to stop it. We know also that some terrible explosions have occurred through the escape of petroleum and therefore it becomes of the utmost importance that vessels intended to contain it should be made absolutely tight and that means thoroughly good work.'

The *Gluckauf* represented excellent workmanship. She was the first tank steamer in the world—her few predecessors in bulk oil transport had been sailing vessels. She discharged her first cargo in July 1886. M. Riedemann immediately placed orders for four more similar vessels, all from Armstrong, Mitchell. In fact almost at once Armstrong, Mitchells became the recognized builders of petrol steamers. From 1886 to 1895 they built more than fifty of them and in the following twenty-five years built another 120, making a total of well over a million tons.

Armstrong's success could be measured by the size that

his firm had now become. For by the early 1890's the engineering works was employing 1,500, the ordance department 3,500 and the shipbuilding department over 2,500. The naval shipyard, with an area of sixteen acres covered over 2,000 feet of river frontage. But, of course, for productive purposes, one must add the Walker yard which contained ten berths and a capacity to turn out 30,000 tons of merchant shipping a year. By this time, the early 'nineties, about 11,000 were employed in normal conditions, swelling to 13,000 during especially busy periods.

Yet these figures represented something of a decline for in 1886 employment had been as high as 16,500 and at the turn of the century was to top 20,000. Many more people were dependent on the works. It was estimated that in the middle 1880's as many as seventy thousand people were directly dependent on the works in one way or another.[5] 'This population forms almost a separate township, with its churches, its schools, science and arts classes, library, literary institute, accident fund, ambulance organization, football, cricket and boating clubs and artillery volunteer corps.'

With its shipyards, its ordnance works, its engineering factories, Tyneside had now become one of the world's greatest centres for the production of weapons of death. Now was beginning to emerge the dreadful paradox that Newcastle was most prosperous in times of peril. For it was then that the factories were busiest, employment greatest and wage rates highest. This paradox was to be seen most graphically in this century, when the two world wars produced boom times which interrupted years of stagnation and decline.

The early signs of the trouble to come could be spotted as early as the 1880's. A report at that time said: 'We are producing less coal ... We are making less iron ... We produce less lead ... We make a smaller quantity of chemicals. Our textile manufactures do not advance as they were wont to do; shipbuilding is only to the extent sufficient to make up the gaps which the ocean makes in the fleets of the world; and though in some branches of machinery we retain our position, we do not make locomotives for the world as we did.'[6] The same report referred to the slowing down of investment. 'Up to twelve years ago, capital in abundance could be had for the asking for the coal and iron mine, the blast furnace and the rolling mill but after that time losses ensued of serious moment, capital became unproductive generally in these industries and it is only in rare cases that there can be found additional money to develop new mines and iron works.' The economic difficulties became so serious that a Royal Commission on the Trade Depression was set up. By the time it reported, the situation was beginning to improve but fundamentally the signs of trouble were there to be seen.

Yet many firms still seemed prosperous. An observer wrote of the Elswick works: 'Their size, their completeness, their tremendous productive energy, their variety of blast furnaces, foundries, machine shops and chemical laboratories, teeming with human life, reverberating with the shriek of steam, the clang of hammers, and the whirr of machinery, overhung by a pillar of cloud by day and of fire by night, present a picture of concentrated industrial activity which overwhelms and astonishes the average observer.'[7] Earlier the same writer observed that Elswick had 'no equal in national importance outside of Woolwich arsenal and finds only one rival in Krupp's of Essen'.

## THE RIVAL, KRUPP

If business generally was booming for Armstrong, it was even better for Krupp. In the ten years from 1853-1863 he had established himself as the world's 'Cannon King'. From that time onwards he widened his domain yet further. No matter what Armstrong did, Krupp always seemed slightly ahead. In the mid-1860's Krupp was so sure of himself that he decided to demolish the whole of his factory, section by section, and rebuild it along the most modern lines, at the same time installing the most modern equipment. He also extended his works. He put in three new rolling mills, three new machine shops, a wheelwright's shop, an axle turnery and a boilershop. Anxious to control his sources of supply, he bought his own coal mines, his own iron-ore beds and his own coking ovens. The business had never been busier, pouring out railway wheels, cast-steel and, above all, guns.

But although hugely prosperous, storm clouds were appearing. Austria and Prussia were beginning to shape up to one another and Krupp's traditional policy of selling to anyone was being increasingly questioned. When Austria placed an order for 24 tons, Bismarck urged him not to accept or at least to postpone delivery. Krupp replied that he must fulfil obligations which he had undertaken. This might be considered an extremely uncharitable, indeed churlish response, considering that Bismark had placed orders with Krupp for 162 four-pounders, 250 six-pounders and 115 twenty-four pounders.

There was worse to come. For although Prussia overwhelmed Austria in seven weeks, thus virtually establishing modern Germany, Krupp cannon had played no significant part. In fact, to be blunt, they had proved a disaster. Gas and flames had leaked from the cannons, making them explode, killing no one but the gunner. The cast-steel, which Krupp preferred, was unsatisfactory. Breeches tended to fly off alarmingly.

His reputation fell. It looked as if the Cannon King had been dethroned. At a time like this, one might have expected a man of his resolution to increase his work at the factory. But Krupp almost never did the usual thing. Instead, at this moment of crisis, he went on holiday and he stayed on holiday for well over a year. His lieutenants were left with the task of restoring prosperity, a task they performed well despite a flow of damning letters from Krupp in his spa resorts.

But Krupp was mainly saved by Karl Siemens who succeeded in devoping the open-hearth furnace in England. This was ideal for impure ores, such as those in the Ruhr, and produced more steel and of a higher quality than the Bessemer process which Krupp had not managed to adapt successfully. Meanwhile his friends within the Army had restored his reputation, largely by improving the breech-loading system.

Within a short period, his overbearing self-confidence had replaced his self-pity. In 1870 France declared war on Prussia —one of the greatest mistakes in history, so unexpected was the result to be. The war completely vindicated Krupp and gave his new reputation a solid foundation. The Prussian Army had 500 Krupp cannon and, according to an eye-witness, the opening days of the war 'already proved the superiority of our artillery to that of the French'. Within five months the war was over. France was humiliated. Prussia—and Krupp —was glorified. Orders now streamed in from all over the world as the reports of the war and the devastating effect of the Krupp cannon were read, indeed devoured. As war fever burst out in many parts of the world—there were 15 conflicts in the 16 years 1871-1887—Krupp benefitted.

The Sino-Japanese war scare of 1874, for example, brought orders from the Chinese for 275 field guns, another 150 cannon and complete armament for eight warships. It was a blow to Armstrong who had been supplying the Chinese. The Krupp factory continued to expand dramatically. In 1870 it employed 10,000. By 1873 that total had gone up by half.

Yet clearly Armstrong was not far behind. For example, he had started his own blast furnaces in 1863. They stood until 1899 when they were pulled down to make way for new shops. But in 1883 he decided that, like Krupp, he should have his own steel works. This important department was started under the management of Colonel Dyer with the intention of supplying gun steel to the Ordnance Works. Within a few years, the capacity was extended to such an extent that large quantities of outside orders were undertaken. They consisted largely of locomotive work, of marine and general castings. Ingots of up to eighty-five tons could be handled by the huge hydraulic presses.

Certainly Armstrong and Krupp could now claim they dominated world armaments between them and that in terms of sheer output or employment figures, there were no other factories to match theirs.

Krupp's output or manpower was slightly greater than Armstrong but he had the enormous advantage of enjoying a monopoly position for the supply to the Prussian Government. In that sense, perhaps the Essen works could be considered as an official arsenal, certainly a semi-official arsenal, rather than as a private enterprise. While Krupp's output was greater, Armstrong's range was wider for he possessed shipyards where the largest naval or mercantile vessels were built. At that time, Elswick was in fact the only factory in the world that could both build and arm warships itself.

Armstrong even opened a branch factory at Pozzuoli on

the bay of Naples to make guns for the Italian Government. Relations with Italy had been close for many years. Now they were to become even closer while the traditions of Elswick were transferred to a totally different environment.

## ARMSTRONG'S IN ITALY

The delivery in 1876 of the *Europa* with its 100-ton gun delighted the Italians. They now possessed the greatest gun in the world. In return, the King created Armstrong Grand Officer of the Order of Saints Maurice and Lazarus. George Rendel and Captain Noble were made Commanders of the Crown of Italy and Stuart Rendel an Officer of the Crown of Italy.

By 1884 Italy decided it wanted to have an armament factory on its own soil under its own ultimate control. Relying on a foreign supplier—even one with which it had such good relations as Armstrong—was potentially dangerous. One could never be absolutely certain that supplies would be forthcoming in the future as they had been in the past. At the same time, the Italian Government had to admit that it had had magnificent service from Armstrong and a better quality product than it could have secured from domestic manufacturers. The Government decided the simple solution was to ask Armstrong to build a branch factory in Italy. At first Armstrong demurred. Would business continue to be good enough to justify such a venture? It would be simpler and better from everyone's point of view to continue to manufacture at Elswick. The Italian Government was adamant. Either a factory was built in Italy or Armstrong's would lose all future orders. Faced with such an ultimatum, Armstrong naturally capitulated. At the same time, capitulation was made easy by the Government's promising a steady stream of orders of sufficient quantity to make the project viable.

An Italian branch factory there was to be, but where? A number of sites were examined. Finally Pozzuoli on the bay of Naples was chosen. About seventy acres were bought near the foundations of Cicero's villa. As soon as this definite step was taken and construction work began, local feeling which had been bubbling up against the foreign firm burst out. The home, manufacturers considered the employment of Armstrong's unpatriotic and almost as dangerous as the previous arrangement. On 6th February 1885 the Minister of Marine faced a barrage of questions in the Chamber of Deputies. He remained calm and resolute. The contract with Armstrong could in no way injure the development of a national industry, he declared. It was a mistake to condemn the arrangement as detrimental to Italy. Indeed, it could be her salvation. The Government should be congratulated, not censured. He was right but for a reason he would not care to give: Armstrong products were far superior to anything Italian manufacturers could supply. To discard Armstrong while other countries continued to buy from him would be sheer folly. The Government would have to ride out the criticism. Armstrong's helped by building the factory in the short period of twelve months. George Rendel, who had resigned from Elswick in 1882, was persuaded to rejoin the company to manage the Italian factory. In fact, he and Admiral Albini were appointed the resident directors. The first launch from the Italian works took place in November 1888.

The Pozzuoli Works, covering sixty-three acres, included ordnance departments and steel works as well as a shipyard. In the first thirty years they turned out over 1,500 naval, field and land service guns for the Italian and other governments. They also constructed a great quantity of naval installations and mountings, coast defence mountings for guns and howitzers and a great amount of shot and shell for the Italian Army and Navy.

## AMALGAMATION WITH MITCHELL

Shortly before the Italian venture was started, Armstrong made a number of critical decisions. He decided to start up his own steel works, to amalgamate with Mitchell's shipbuilding firm and to turn the company from a private one into a public one. While each decision was important in itself, they were linked together. For with the development of new steel-making techniques, Armstrong could see a need to possess his own means of supply as well as the possibility of entering an expanding market. Steel would be used increasingly for ships as well as guns. The close ties with Mitchell's Walker yard had produced many benefits. A formal link was more than desirable. Yet continuing expansion plans, particularly for the steel works, would need substantial funding—more than Armstrong and most of his associates felt they wanted to bear. The public should be invited to contribute. These decisions brought a quickening in the firm's growth. They also led to the resignation of one of Armstrong's closest colleagues, George Rendel.

It was in November 1882 that Sir William Armstrong and Dr Charles Mitchell agreed to unite their two businesses. A new company, Sir W. G. Armstrong, Mitchell and Co Ltd, was established to take over the stocks, buildings, tools and goodwill of the two separate firms at a cost of £1,575,000.

Partly to finance this operation but mainly to finance the new steel works, the new company decided immediately to offer shares to the public. It set its capital at £2 million in 20,000 shares of £100 each, of which 18,500 were to be offered immediately. A local paper commented: 'Vast as is the present capacity of the Elswick Works, the addition of a great steel-working plant will largely add to its ability to afford remunerative employment to a large body of workmen ... "Armstrong Town" is even at present a sufficiently lively and prosperous locality but with such an accession of business as the new company promises to set in operation it must increase in wealth and importance.'[8] It did and the shares reflected the prosperity. Within a short time, the price was double the face value. No wonder when a dividend of nine per cent was paid in the first year! A contemporary comment was: 'As a public company Elswick has increased and advanced with even greater energy than before.'[9]

It did so without the help of George Rendel who resigned from the company, at least temporarily. He had been with Armstrong for twenty-five years, indeed had lived under his roof for a time and was treated by Armstrong almost like a son. Yet not quite. At least he found Armstrong had an equal favourite in Captain Andrew Noble, a person who despite his great scientific and managerial qualities, Rendel loathed. Other people did too. Noble indeed was difficult to like. He was overbearing, he was arrogant, he was interfering. To Armstrong he showed a milder side of his nature and no doubt this explains how he managed to persuade Armstrong to give him sole charge of the Ordnance Works at the managerial reshuffle following the amalgamation. Until then, Rendel and Noble had been joint managers.

Stuart Rendel recorded that Captain Noble had 'become so dissatisfied and melancholy as to, at last, rouse Sir W. G. Armstrong's sympathy to the unhappy extent of causing Sir W. G. Armstrong to invite George Rendel to transfer to Sir A. Noble the managership of the Ordnance Department.' George Rendel decided to leave the company and became Civil Lord of the Admiralty. Brother Stuart had already resigned. In 1880 he had become a Liberal Member of Parliament.

The Rendels not only disliked Noble. They disliked the amalgamation with Mitchell's and turning the company into a public one. But out of friendship to Armstrong to whom they were devoted—although the reverse did not seem to be quite the case—they kept their views largely to themselves. As we have seen, George Rendel actually returned to the company's service by taking on the managership of the Italian factory. But after Armstrong's death, the battle between Noble and the Rendels came into the open. They complained of the 'needless million' which the firm had put into 'the Mitchell and Swan pockets over the purchase of Low Walker, only to find Low Walker a grievous loss and perpetual embarrassment.' They complained of Noble trying to do everyone's work including that of the London manager 'at the cost of innumerable night journeys, transacting all the London business himself from lodgings or his club in London.'

In fact the feud did not die down until 1911 when the sides signed : 'a solemn Treaty between the Executive Directors and the independent directors under which the Executive Directors implicitly pledged their honour to effect certain specified introductions of new blood in the executive and on the Board provided the independent directors would accept responsibility for the Executive Directors' irregularities for many years past in secretly appropriating to themselves exceptionally large remunerations and would further sanction certain very liberal remunerations in future.' So much for Victorian and Edwardian rectitude!

Despite the internal disputes, the public image of the company was very high—and with good reason. Net profits of Armstrong, Mitchell and Co. Ltd, rose steadily for the first nine years of the life of the public company. They went from £141,000 in 1883 to £239,000 in 1891. They then dropped back slightly but by 1895 they were up to £252,000 and went on rising. The dividends during these years ranged from 7¾ per cent to 11¾ per cent per annum. Quite simply, Armstrong and his works were regarded as national symbols, signifying at once the military might, the scientific excellence and the managerial enterprise of Britain at its best.

# CHAPTER EIGHT

LIKE his father before him, Armstrong showed no practical interest in politics until old age. Even then, it was not politics in general but one specific issue that generated his enthusiasm. Whereas his father had become engrossed in the responsibility of local government and had taken a full part in the affairs of Newcastle Council, it was the issue of Irish Home Rule and that alone which brought Sir William Armstrong into the political arena in 1886. Before then, two or three requests had been made to him by both the Conservative and Liberal parties to stand as their candidate at a general election. He stoutly refused to do so. In 1883 such a strong rumour started that he was to be put forward that he found it necessary to issue the following statement to the Press:

'To go into Parliament at my time of life is about the last thing I would consent to do, even for Newcastle. In the first place, London life and Parliamentary hours would be more than I could bear and, in the second place, being too progressive for one party and too conservative for the other, I fear I should eventually illustrate the case of falling between two stools.'

The question of Home Rule for Ireland, which was then becoming the dominant issue in British politics and to which the Prime Minister, William Gladstone, had just become thoroughly converted, was to seize Armstrong so strongly that he was to change his mind within three years. Although a moderate Liberal all his life, Armstrong was one of the many members of the party who could not follow Gladstone's sudden conversion and indeed felt they should do all in their power to oppose him on this question. The party split into Gladstonian Liberals, who followed their leader in backing Home Rule as the only effective, permanent answer to the Irish Question, and the Unionist Liberals, led by Hartington, who associated themselves with the Conservative Party in opposing the proposal.

Newcastle reflected the national fragmentation. For the 1886 Election, called after the defeat of Gladstone's Home Rule Bill, there were to be four candidates for the two seats: two Gladstone Liberals, and a Unionist Liberal siding with the Conservative candidate. The Unionist Liberal was Armstrong. A committee of Unionists under the chairmanship of Dr Thomas Hodgkin had been formed a few weeks before the election and as soon as the Government was defeated, started to look earnestly for a candidate. Armstrong was a natural choice. He was the greatest industrialist in the region, a man of international reputation and a firm opponent of Home Rule. It was decided to approach him to stand.

He agreed to do so if a sufficiently large number of people signed a petition requesting him to. A petition was drawn up immediately along these lines: 'We, the undersigned electors of the city of Newcastle upon Tyne, believing that the presence of our most eminent citizen in Parliament will be of great service to the country at the present crisis, respectfully request you to stand as a candidate for the representation of the city at the approaching General Election; and we pledge ourselves to use every exertion to secure your return.'

The petition was available at six premises in the city and advertisements were taken in the local press urging supporters to sign. Armstrong's conditional consent to stand was in complete contrast to his previous answers when asked to do so—the *Newcastle Daily Journal* called his change of mind 'a sensation'—but Home Rule was an issue that stirred him so deeply he felt unable now to decline. Within a few days over 5,000 signatures had been put to the petition. Dr Thomas Hodgkin, chairman of the Newcastle and Northumberland Unionist Liberal Association, went to Cragside to give Armstrong the news. As expected, Armstrong agreed to stand but he did impose three conditions. He wanted to be excused 'on the ground of feeble health', from canvassing. He refused to pledge himself on any political question apart from total opposition to Home Rule. Thirdly, 'As I shall be quite unable to stand the wear and tear of habitual Parliamentary life, I can only undertake to attend important divisions.'

Normally such conditions would have been totally un-
acceptable particularly in what was clearly going to be a
closely-fought contest, but it was felt that Armstrong's
eminence would offset such practical difficulties. His agreement to stand was met with acclaim.

The *Newcastle Daily Journal* said the conditions would be
'cheerfully agreed to by his supporters'. By Thursday, 17th
June, the four candidates for Newcastle's two seats had been
named. Alongside the Moderate Liberal, Sir William Armstrong, would stand Sir Matthew White Ridley, a Conservative. Like Armstrong, he was totally opposed to Home Rule. In
fact, the dominating influence of this one issue above all
others led the Newcastle Conservative Association to greet
Armstrong's candidature with enthusiasm. Despite their
different party labels, Armstrong and Riley were to be allies.
Against them stood Mr John Morley, a former Minister, and
Mr James Craig, both of whom were whole-hearted supporters
of Home Rule.

The campaign began on 18th June and everyone knew it
was going to be a fierce campaign, the toughest of the century.
With an issue that divided the country so deeply and so
evenly, the victory would go to the side that canvassed hardest,
organized best, worked longest. In such circumstances, the tension mounted day after day.

Armstrong began his campaign on Friday, 18th June, when
he read his address to his supporters in the large dining room
of the Central Station Hotel. He declared: 'Acting under a
sense of duty at a great national crisis, I yield to the urgent
solicitation of a large section of my fellow-citizens to allow
myself to be nominated at the approaching election. The one
question of the day is that relating to the future government
of Ireland. On that question I declare myself the decided
opponent of any scheme which may lead to the disintegration
of the Empire, or involve the desertion of the loyal party in
Ireland, whose numbers are veiled by the terrorism which
prevents the free assertion of individual opinion when opposed
to the dominant faction in that country. I should, however,
be quite prepared to entertain any well-considered scheme of
local self-government for Ireland such as would be consistent
with the complete supremacy of the Imperial Parliament and

the protection of the law-abiding portion of the community. On all other topics, should you do me the honour of returning me, I shall enter Parliament pledged only to pursue such a course of action as shall accord with the tenor of my past life, which has been that of a Moderate Liberal, desirous to promote the welfare of the great body of my countrymen.'

Armstrong's short address was warmly received. *The Journal* called it 'modest, judicious and to the point'. On the following evening, a large meeting of Armstrong's supporters met in the Northumberland Hall—so large a meeting in fact that Armstrong prophesied: 'I think you have made an excellent start. There has been very great enthusiasm displayed on this occasion; and I feel confident that, through your kind exertions, my candidature is tolerably safe.'

That was putting things too optimistically although he was no doubt swept away on the waves of excitement. The Unionist Liberals, who had come together on an ad hoc basis, had a great problem in the lack of effective organization covering the whole city. They adopted the obvious solution of co-operating with the Conservative Association. The two committees, and indeed their supporters, were to remain distinct but for all practical help, they would act as one. This was a vital agreement. Without it, the fight would have been a much tougher one, perhaps impossible. And a fight it certainly was. The *Newcastle Daily Leader*, a staunch supporter of Gladstone and Home Rule, led the attack day after day. While acknowledging that Armstrong was 'the most honoured name in the North country', it declared that he was being led astray by 'a small section of people' who, while claiming that he 'deserves a seat in Parliament because of his private virtues' were really 'seeking shelter under his name ... because they want to defeat Mr Gladstone's efforts to give Home Rule to Ireland'. The paper called it 'a most audacious piece of political dodgery', but it overlooked the fact that Armstrong was a resolute and known opponent of Home Rule and felt so strongly on the topic that he believed he should do everything he could to prevent it. He was not made a candidate against his will. He had turned down previous requests to put himself forward and now at 76 could have been expected to turn down another request even more firmly. But he wanted to stand. Nor did he

hide the fact, as we have seen, that his only policy declaration
was on the question of Home Rule. For the rest, he would act
as a moderate Liberal. Armstrong, the Unionist Liberals in
Newcastle and the public all knew exactly why he was standing and what support for him would represent. The charge of
political dodgery seems unfair but such was the atmosphere
of that campaign.

On 24th June, Armstrong made a long speech at the Circus
outlining his position. He pointed out that he had no political
experience or training but that as a successful businessman he
had been used to examining serious and complicated matters
carefully and quietly. He had therefore examined the proposal
for Home Rule and felt that such a solution would not solve
any of the political and social difficulties in that country.
Gladstone, he felt, had made 'the most unwarrantable
surrender of pledges. Instead of calm reasoning we have had
passionate orations and instead of candour we have had party
manoeuvring to which the great Liberal Party should never
have descended.' And the cause of it all was Gladstone himself. Without Gladstone's backing, Home Rule would not
muster twenty supporters in Parliament. It was his personal
power and authority that was the main stimulus. 'But if Mr
Gladstone succeeds by his personal influence in carrying this
measure, there will be nothing beyond his power to do in
future. He will become a dictator, with an army of disciplined
adherents at his back, determined to support him in every
political enterprise however reckless it may be.'

One of the 'disciplined adherents', John Morley, was standing in Newcastle. He had spoken in brilliant fashion a couple
of days previously at the Town Hall—a speech punctuated
with laughter, applause and cheers throughout its two hours.
The Daily Leader commented: 'Mr Morley's speech was one
of the most powerful expositions of the Irish Question which
has yet been delivered.'

By contrast, Armstrong's speeches were few, grew shorter
and shorter and aroused little reaction. He was not, of course,
an experienced orator. He was used to speaking in public but
not on political matters where the subject as well as the atmosphere was more highly charged than in the scientific circles
he was used to. His age, too, prevented him from making more

Cragside : exterior view.

Drawing Rm., Craigie.

than a rather perfunctory round of half a dozen speeches in the main suburbs of the city. This lack of total commitment may well have been the deciding issue on polling day, 5th July.

Although the campaign was close right to the end, the Gladstone Liberals triumphed. Armstrong and Ridley were defeated. The result was:

| | |
|---|---|
| Morley | 10,681 |
| Craig | 10,172 |
| Armstrong | 9,657 |
| Ridley | 9,580 |

Immediately after the declaration of the poll an enormous crowd of Liberal supporters rushed along Collingwood Street and up Pilgrim Street to form a dense mass in front of the Liberal Club. Morley addressed them there, declaring that, 'the Liberal party in Newcastle has gained one of its most glorious victories'.

Armstrong meanwhile drove quietly in a covered carriage to his central committee rooms in Grainger Street. He too made a short speech. 'I have the satisfaction of thinking that in having come forward, I have done my duty.' he said. This view was not shared by the *Daily Leader*, which now made its most bitter attack upon him. 'His political speeches showed that he had not studied even the rudiments of the subject under discussion and his age rendered him incapable of sustaining without hurt to himself the turmoil of a contested election.' He could take consolation that the *Daily Leader's* comments about his associate, Ridley, were even stronger. 'His speeches have been the very poorest sort of stuff ... He has shown how far a little talent can go in one's position as a country gentleman and how poorly it figures in a city election.'[2]

Armstrong had lost some of his personal reputation as a result of the election. After all, his own standing and authority were his main political assets, as far as the Unionist Liberal Association was concerned. Clearly they had not proved enough. He had not got quite as much personal prestige and pulling power as was imagined.

The Conservative *Newcastle Daily Journal* commented: 'It

would be idle not to admit that the result of the election for
the city declared yesterday was a great and even a bitter disappointment to the losing party.' The paper acknowledged the
ability and eminence of one of the Liberal candidates, John
Morley, but added that the disappointment was so great
because the Tories and Unionists had brought in two candidates whose popularity was so high that it seemed impossible
to their supporters that they could lose.' But there was consolation to be had in the national results. For while the Home
Rulers triumphed in Newcastle, they did not do so in the
country at large, where the Conservative and Unionist Liberals
gained a majority of well over a hundred. For Armstrong the
election was bitterly disappointing but there opened up within
a year a new entry into Parliament. For in the Queen's Jubilee
Honours list of 1887 he was made a peer. The announcement
was not altogether a surprise. A number of local papers had
hinted at it a few weeks before but when the news was
officially released on 20th June 1887 it was greeted enthusiastically. Even the *Newcastle Daily Leader* that had criticized
Armstrong's election campaign felt moved to comment: 'So
long as such honours are given, it is men like our townsman
who deserve to get and who are able worthily to wear them.
He has done distinguished service to his country. He has
carried the burden of a great success with a singular modesty
which comes alone from quiet consciousness of strength. There
is no one in these northern counties today who will not receive
the announcement of his elevation as they would greet good
news of a personal friend.'[3] It is surely extraordinary how a
year can change one's views!

A fortnight later, at the beginning of July, Armstrong, now
Lord Armstrong of Cragside, was one of the principal guests
at a dinner given by the Northern Liberal Unionist Association. He spoke of Ireland and of the need for a new party to
be formed composed of people of good sense. 'I think generally
there is no great difference between sensible men,' he said
'that is, men of ordinary good judgement, and if such men of
all parties would band themselves into a party—a strong and
powerful party—to suppress the recklessness, the incon-
sistency, the passion of the struggle for power which is now
rampant in the House of Commons, they would best serve the

interests of this country.' It was a popular line, the sort of criticism that has been made against politicians at many periods and it earned Armstrong a cheer. But politics is about power, about persuasion and about a struggle for putting one's own view. That indeed was what Armstrong himself was attempting. It was his own 'passion' over the Irish Question that had brought him into the political arena. The passion for power of one sort or another is an inevitable part of politics.

Armstrong continued to speak on the Irish Question when the opportunity arose and he attended every debate on the subject in the House of Lords. But his interest in politics never widened into a general one. It was Home Rule and Home Rule only that excited him politically. He did however represent Rothbury on Northumberland County Council from 1889 to 1892 but generally his interest in politics waned as quickly as it had risen. The final years of his life, as so many of those that had gone before, were devoted to scientific matters.

## ARMSTRONG AND COMPANY ON SHOW

The Great Exhibition in Hyde Park, London, in 1851 started a fashion which swept around the world: the staging of great international exhibitions. Before then, there had, of course, been great public fairs in many of the principal cities of England and Europe. There had been, too, national exhibitions. But the 1851 Exhibition widened the scope by allowing other countries to display their achievements in contrast to those of the host country. The trick was brilliantly effective for Britain was able to demonstrate in convincing fashion before a world audience her superiority in most forms of manufacture. The success was so large, other countries quickly adopted the new style. In the next thirty-five years, no fewer than 140 major international exhibitions were staged throughout the world. One of them was held in Newcastle in 1887 to celebrate Queen Victoria's jubilee. The object: 'To still further extend, if possible, the city's name and fame and, by the powerful aid of competition and comparison, to give and receive increased instruction in modern science and art.' The exhibition spread over 31 acres with a huge building in the centre which in itself enclosed a square of two and a quarter acres. Although primarily an industrial exhibition with comprehensive exhibits from the shipbuilding, engineering, chemical, mining, iron and steel industries, it had much else on display too. There was the best collection of paintings ever assembled in the North of England. There was a theatre which seated 1,500 people. And there was a large-scale replica of the old Tyne Bridge that had been partly swept away by flood in 1781.

Among the principal exhibitors and certainly one of the greatest sources of local pride was the firm of Sir W. G. Armstrong, Mitchell and Co Ltd, which put on display many items representing its ordnance or shipbuilding interests. Armstrong himself liked exhibitions and he went to many of them during his life. It was a very useful way, he thought, not only of seeing what other people, some of them rivals, were doing but also of making contacts. He had taken part, for example, in the exhibition of arts, manufactures and practical science held in Newcastle in 1840 before he had even set up his own company. He put on show then his 'Water pressure wheel for obtaining direct rotary motion from the pressure of a column of water.' It attracted a great deal of attention, including this doggerel from a local poet:

> 'Says aw, 'Why Armstrong thou's a king,
> Thou'll sure gie Hudson's steam the fling.'

He also took part in the 1848 Exhibition with an improved model of his water pressure engine. Now almost 40 years later, his manufactures dominated the Royal Jubilee Exhibition. As one reporter put it: 'Our attention is rivetted by the unparalleled exhibits of the Ordnance manufactured at the Elswick works.'

The central attraction was the 110-ton gun, the most powerful piece of ordnance in the world, of which a full-sized model was shown. Constructed entirely of steel, the Gun had been made for the British Government for the armament of first-class ships of war. Two of them were about to be fitted to H.M.S. *Victoria* then being built at Elswick. Each was 44 feet long with a sixteen inch bore and capable of firing a shot weighing 1,800 lbs.

In constrast stood the Gatling Gun of one and a half cwts, for which Armstrong, Mitchell were the English manufacturers. Between these two extremes came a dazzling range of different purposes: mountain guns, howitzers, rapid-fire guns of various kinds and, of course, big guns. In addition, there were separate exhibits of some of the more interesting component parts, the steel breech-block, which resisted the explosion of the charge; the hydraulic rammer which replaced human labour for pushing the great weights of powder and shell into the bore; non-recoil carriages and new mounting designs.

The shipbuilding exhibits were equally impressive. The firm displayed sixty models or photographs of its naval and mercantile output. There were models of the various fast protected cruisers built for Italy or Japan, of frigates sold to Russia and gunboats sold to China. There were models of the oil tankers, an Armstrong invention, of troopships and steamers and the full range of the vast output. It was a 'unique' collection according to a local newspaper and it attracted a unique crowd. Over 100,000 people paid for admission on the first day, Wednesday, 11th May. Never before had such a crowd assembled in Newcastle. 'Proceeding along the grassy footing, there was nothing but elbowing through the throng for hundreds of yards,' one correspondent wrote. On the following day, His Royal Highness the Duke of Cambridge, who performed the opening ceremony, and the official party visited the Elswick factory to see in still greater detail the work that was being done there. They saw many pieces of cannon in the process of construction, and the powerful steam hammers, lathes, rifling machines, with which they were made. After lunch, the party went on a more expensive tour by railway, visiting the steel works, the shipyard and the general engineering shops. It was a very impressive tour and the Duke, who also happened to be the Commander-in-Chief of the British Army, left 'secure in the knowledge that Britain's safety was assured by the work you are doing here'. That safety was to be further assured by the amalgamation of Armstrong's firm with that of his old rival, Sir Joseph Whitworth.

## AMALGAMATION WITH WHITWORTH

By this time, the mid-1890's, the firm of Sir W. G. Armstrong, Mitchell and Co Ltd, had grown to enormous proportions. Each of the four departments was a major factory in its own right. The Engine Works, from which all the rest had sprung, were still doing a good business in steam pumping engines, swing bridges, dock gates and hydraulic machinery generally. About 2,000 men were employed in these works alone. Then, the most famous of the departments, the Ordnance Works, were still very busy, turning out heavy guns, naval artillery and projectiles of all kinds. The average weekly output of ammunition consisted of 2,000 six-inch cases, 1,300 4-7-inch cases, 1,000 12-pounder cases, 2,500 three-pounder and six-pounder cases. There were 1,300 guns of various calibres in course of manufacture. At that time, too, the Shipyard had a terrifying output under construction, consisting of:

|  | Displacement Tons |
|---|---|
| One armour-clad battleship | 12,200 |
| Two first-class armoured cruisers each | 9,600 |
| Two first-class armoured cruisers each | 8,000 |
| One fast protected cruiser | 4,500 |
| Two fast protected cruisers | 4,300 |
| Two armour-clads | 3,800 |
| One fast protected cruiser | 3,600 |
| Two fast protected cruisers, each | 3,450 |
| One third-class cruiser | 2,800 |

Meanwhile, the Steel Works, using the Siemen's process, were turning out 500-600 tons of steel a week while the Walker shipyard was capable of launching 50,000 tons of merchant shipping a year.

Just short of 20,000 men were employed at this time and the total wages bill in a year topped £1.5 million. These are staggering figures. They become even more staggering when one takes into account the size of families in those days. Considering that there was nothing unusual about families of twelve children, one could conservatively estimate six children per family showing that well over 100,000 people were directly dependent on the works. At least twice as many again would be in some considerable degree dependent upon the firm's success.

By comparison, the Manchester works of Sir Joseph Whitworth and Co Ltd, employed about a tenth of that number, just short of 2,000 in fact. Yet it was a most important company. New works had been built at Openshaw, two miles from the original works, in 1880 covering 40 acres. Here in modern conditions a wide range of products was made from machine tools of the largest size or gauges of the finest precision to armour plate of the toughest resistance and gun mountings of the easiest manoeuvrability.

The armour plate department, in particular, was exceptionally good. In fact, it was generally regarded as the most modern in the world. Perhaps this is no surprise for armour plate production was Whitworth's main preoccupation in later life. In 1879, after a series of exhaustive experiments he produced his 'impregnable armour plating' formed of fluid pressed steel, built up in ringed hexagonal sections. In trials held at Southport a 250 lb. shell was fired from a nine-inch gun at 30 yards range against a nine-inch target of this plating. The shell drove the target back about 18 inches into the sandbank against which it was placed, but only penetrated 1½ inches into the plating. The success led to large-scale development of this side of the company's work but it was one of a number of companies involved for there was great international rivalry in armour plate.

Whitworth's works, with their interest in ordnance and steel making were thus closely parallel to those of Armstrong. During Whitworth's life, there could of course be no thought of anything but competition between the two firms. But Whitworth had died in 1887, ten years previously. The personal battle between the two men had been a long time ago. Many things had changed since then. New and powerful rivals had emerged, such as the firm of Vickers. A merger between Armstrong's firm and that left behind by Whitworth had much to commend it, particularly since the Sheffield firm of Vickers, originally an iron and steel works, had now entered the armament business partly through developing its own all-steel armour plate and partly through a small government order for guns. When in 1897 Vickers bought the Naval Construction and Armaments Company Limited at Barrow for £425,000 so that it could supply ships complete with engines, guns and machinery and then followed this up in the same year by buying the automatic machine gun firm of Maxim Nordenfelts for £1.3 millions, Armstrong's could no longer shut their eyes to the fact that they now had a very serious and efficient competitor. As Stuart Rendel wrote later: 'Vickers were modern if anything. They have all the conditions and dispositions we lack.'

At the same time, the demand for armaments in general and warships in particular was rising rapidly. Events abroad— the establishment of a Russian squadron in the Mediterranean, the growing seapower of Japan, Germany's increased naval programme—all represented genuine threats to Britain's naval supremacy. Accordingly, the Naval Estimates for 1896-7 rose to £22 million, of which £7m represented new construction work.

Under these circumstances, the search for new capacity was a natural step and the merger of the two formerly rival firms no longer seemed as preposterous as it once would have done.

In 1895 Armstrong's had increased its share capital to three million pounds and in 1897 it bought Sir Joseph Whitworth and Co Ltd outright. For the Tyneside firm, the merger represented a large increase in steel-making capacity, in ordnance production and in the output of gun carriage. It also brought new techniques for armour plate manufacture and new knowledge of precision engineering of the highest quality. All this extra capacity was sorely needed to match the continuing rises in naval demands—by 1901 the Estimates for new naval construction were above nine million pounds and a large part of the work came to the new firm of Armstrong, Whitworth.

The merger was the last important business transaction undertaken by Lord Armstrong, the former solicitor who had started a small hydraulic business on five acres of land, employing 20 men. Now his firm was one of the greatest in the world with offshoots at Manchester and in Italy. The Tyneside works alone covered 250 acres and employed over 20,000 men. For the past few years Armstrong himself had been no more than a guiding spirit called on when fundamental decisions, such as the merger with Whitworths, were to be taken. Otherwise he left matters to Noble and the others. As he shrugged off these business interests Armstrong returned to his laboratory and took up again his experiments in electricity.

## EXPERIMENTS WITH ELECTRICITY

These experiments had formed his first entry into the world of science when he developed his hydro-electric machine. He always described it as 'my first electrical love'. But he had set electrical studies to one side and plunged into hydraulics, ordnance and the development of Elswick. This in itself adds to the stature of the man for to forsake one's prime interest for another indicates a selfless, perhaps even a ruthless objectivity, which many would find difficult to follow. Not until 1892 did he find enough time to be able to take up his electrical studies again. The following year he lectured to the Literary and Philosophical Society in Newcastle on the subject, speaking and demonstrating for almost two hours. It was a remarkable achievement for someone then aged 83. But age had not yet become a burden to him, as a glance at a typical week illustrates. On one Monday morning at this time he left Cragside at 6.30 and drove over the moors to Alnwick, where he changed horses before going on to Adderstone. There he spent the rest of that and the whole of the following day in land surveying. On the Wednesday he breakfasted at 6.30, drove to Belford and travelled by train to London. Thursday was spent in transacting business. On Friday he returned to Cragside and on Saturday he worked in his laboratory from 9.0 a.m. to 7.0 p.m.

For his lecture he talked about the 'Novel Effects of the Electric Discharge'. But before he began this lecture, part of the Literary and Philosophical Society's centenary celebrations, he reminded the very large audience that his father had been a founder member so that the membership of father and son, taken together, spanned the entire century of the Society's existence. He himself had lectured there on a number of occasions, the first time being forty-nine years previously when he had demonstrated his first hydro-electric machine.

Throughout the mid-1890's he continued his electrical experiments in his laboratory at Cragside and in 1897 published the results in a book, *Electric Movement in Air and Water*. This work, declared *The Times*, 'embodies one of the most remarkable contributions to physical and electrical knowledge that have been made in recent years. It is nearly twenty-five years since Lord Kelvin first formed his conception of matter as "the vortex motion of an everywhere-present fluid". It has fallen to Lord Armstrong's lot to demonstrate his experimental results of surpassing beauty that, in the domain of electricity, vortex motion, in all probability, plays a hitherto unsuspected part.'

Using a large Wimshurst machine, Armstrong was able to have photographs taken of a perfection and minuteness of detail previously unparalleled. They provided the evidence for his theory that electrical energy operates in a vortex.

He described his introduction to the subject like this: 'More than half a century ago, when using my large hydro-electric machine, before it went to the Polytechnic Institution, I hit upon a remarkable experiment.' He connected two wine glasses, filled to the brim with chemically pure water, by a cotton thread, coiled up in one glass but with the short end dipping into the other. The two glasses were joined up to the machine, one with a negative, the other with a positive lead. When the machine was put into action, the coiled thread quickly left the negative vessel and fell into the positive one, leaving for a few moments a rope of water about a third of an inch in length suspended between the lips of the two glasses. His new researches developed this work much further.

He suggested that the behaviour of the electrical discharge indicated the co-existence of two opposite currents in the movements of electricity, the negative being surrounded by the positive, like a core within a tube. After describing the experiment in detail, he wrote:

'The salient impression which all this leaves on my mind is that electricity is identical with the inherent motion of molecules. There can be no such thing as motionless electricity ... Faraday has said that there is probably as much electricity in a single drop of water as would produce a thunderstorm if free. I see no reason to dispute it ... It may well be doubted whether molecules themselves are anything more than specialized motions. We only recognize them by the forces and we know of nothing else to represent their substance and their inertia.' Motion, he felt, might be considered as the 'absolute' of matter.

'These views of the structural capacity of motion present Nature under a more spiritual aspect than one of crude Materialism; and while they lead us to contemplate her wonders with increased amazement, they make her appear more akin to an Infinite Dominant Mind.'

The remarkable photographs in the book were taken by a local photographer, John Worsnop of Rothbury, who had become a close friend of Armstrong's. Years later, Worsnop recalled : 'There was ample scope in the great field of electricity for the exercise of his mighty intellect and the patience, perseverance and dogged determination, the fertility of resource and intense enthusiasm with which he pursued his researches filled one with wonder and admiration. He never seemed to tire and often regretted his inability of accomplish more work. The working hours were from 9.0 a.m. until 7.30 p.m. and when there were no guests staying in the house, he frequently allowed himself only ten minutes for dinner and then went on working till 9.30 ! The work was wholly experimental and many difficulties were encountered; but difficulties only increased his enthusiasm and stimulated his energies; he revelled in them and his efforts never ceased till he conquered and overcame them.'

It was for his great services to scientific invention that he was rewarded by many distinctions. He received honorary degrees from Oxford, Cambridge, Durham and Dublin and was at one time or another president of the British Association for the Advancement of Science, of the Mechanical Engineers, the North of England Mining and Mechanical Engineers, the Institute of Civil Engineers, the Literary and Philosophical Society of Newcastle and of the Natural History Society of Northumberland, Durham and Newcastle.

But even his amazing physical and mental energies were beginning to wane. He was increasingly confined to the house. He found himself taking longer naps after meals and unable to concentrate with quite the same power as previously. He made fewer trips to Newcastle or London and fewer people came to see him at Cragside. His wife, Margaret, had died in September 1893, and from that time onwards some of the spirit seemed to go out of him too.

## THE DEATH OF ARMSTRONG

Armstrong died at ten minutes past one o'clock in the morning of Thursday, 27th December, 1900. He had been poorly for some time. Indeed he had not really been well since the autumn of that year. But at the beginning of December he gradually grew worse and was confined to bed. Over the next few days a fever developed and grew stronger. At the same time he found it increasingly difficult to eat and eventually he was unable to take any food at all. This, together with his great age—he had past his 90th birthday—made it impossible for him to rally from the attack.

He passed away peacefully, so peacefully in fact that it was difficult to tell exactly when he had died. He had fallen asleep early on the previous morning and had never regained consciousness. At five in the evening it was thought that the end had come but he rallied and slumbered quietly until just after one o'clock in the following morning. His grand-nephew and niece, his heirs, Mr and Mrs Watson-Armstrong, were in the room. So were Andrew Crozier, his valet, John Bertram, his steward, and the two professional nurses who had been at Cragside several weeks.

A few hours later, at seven-thirty, the solemn tolling of the Rothbury church bell conveyed the message of his death to the local people. The flag was also hung at half-mast. But there was a thick mist about that morning so that few would have seen it hanging.

Not only the local but also the national newspapers published long biographical articles, together with editorial comments. *The Times* said : 'By the death of Lord Armstrong, England loses one of those eminent citizens who, from a private station, exercise an influence over national life deeper and more far-reaching than is wielded, save in rare and exceptional cases, by the politicians who engross public attention.' It then went on to contrast the advances made possible

by Armstrong's work with the disheartening and blind
attitude shown by Government officials, particularly with
regard to breech action of guns. Where other countries overcame the difficulties at first experienced in breech action, this
country had used those difficulties as an excuse to return to
muzzle-loading, thus falling dangerously behind the rest of the
world.

'We can now turn out guns and machinery at least equal
to any in the world,' declared The Times, 'but now, as
previously our Government is not always alive to the
importance of being abreast of the age. It is still an uphill fight
to get new ideas recognized before some emergency like the
South African war forces us to re-arm in a hurry. But we may
muddle through so long as we have a succession of private
citizens like Lord Armstrong, capable of applying every
advance made by science. It is largely by such men that the
Empire has been made and defended and it is mainly by such
men that its safety must be assured in the future.'

The Newcastle Daily Journal took an even more
sympathetic view of his life and work and even went so far
as to edge its pages in thick black type. 'There is another great
man the less in our midst this morning,' the leader column
began. But clearly the paper was not taken by surprise for it
printed an extensive biography, together with its commentary
on the same day as Armstrong died; indeed the paper was
published within a few hours of his death. 'Lord Armstrong
has won his fame and reputation by no merely showy exploits,
by no meretricious and fleeting notoriety. His is not a name
that is acclaimed today, to be forgotten by tomorrow. He is
one of those who added materially and permanently to the
practical advancement of the race in its conquest of the
physical world.' Not once in the two-thousand word obituary
does a balancing word of the effects of Armstrong's work
appear. It is all glory, wisdom and fairmindedness.

The Newcastle Daily Chronicle took a more objective view.
After listing the achievements and passing the usual tributes,
it then observed: 'Lord Armstrong may be best remembered
in the end, by the world at large, as a strangely representative
figure of the latest phase of nineteenth century civilization. On
the one hand, we have the most wonderful machinery of

production that has ever been known; on the other, we have
the most tremendous machinery of murder. We subject the
rudest powers of nature to the service of peace and we employ
the most refined powers of the intellect to devise methods of
destruction more awful than flood or earthquake ... The
inventor of hydraulic machinery, the inventor of the hydro-
electric machine, and life-long student of electric phenomena,
was a pioneer in the direct utilization of water power and in
the efforts to connect water power with electric energy which
have resulted in the harnessing of Niagara. But the inventor
of the new artillery; the designer of the most colossal of
weapons, the 110-ton gun; the director of the Elswick arsenal
was no less a pioneer of the modern armaments which seem
to threaten a decimation of mankind in the battle of Arma-
geddon. There is something that appals the imagination in the
cool application of a clear and temperate mind like Lord Armstrong's to the science of destruction.' Yet, the paper con-
cluded, the very advances of military prowess might reduce
rather than increase the chances of war and wholesale destruction. 'The world if never so equipped for war was never so
reluctant to make it. The sight of means to do ill-deeds all
round keeps the ill-deeds undone.'

This argument was repeated in at least one of the church
sermons the following Sunday in Newcastle. Speaking in St
Thomas's Church, Dr A. J. Harrison told his very large con-
gregation: 'The wonderful genius of Lord Armstrong might,
perhaps, prove to be an aid to peace rather than to war; it
might be that the weapons of destruction would become so
great that no nation would venture upon a campaign of war.'

The *Newcastle Daily Leader*, which had criticized his
election campaign in 1886, was also slightly less warm than
other papers in its tribute to him. It said: 'We shall not claim
for Lord Armstrong the highest rank. That would be to do him
an injustice. He lacked that higher sympathy which draws
and subdues all classes of men ... His conception of the relations between the classes was shaped more by economic laws
than by warm feelings. His outlook, also, on the broad world
of politics was not that of the highest minds. A partisan he
never was in the strictest sense of the word. At the same time,
he was not free from the bias of class and one cannot associate

him with the elect of the ages who have striven and nobly
suffered for the race. But nothwithstanding these limitations
he was a great man whose service to the world will give him
a high place among the master builders of the century.'
This judgement seems a little harsh. It is surely not only
those who 'suffer for the race' or who possess that 'higher
sympathy which draws and subdues all classes' that deserve
to be considered in the highest rank. A scientist who enlarges
the human understanding of the mysteries of the world or who
significantly reduces human labour or improves the material
lot of man also could claim to be considered in the highest
rank.

The funeral service took place on Monday, 31st December
1900 in Rothbury Parish Church. It was not as well attended
as had been expected—the special trains run from Newcastle
were not full. No doubt the miserable weather was to blame.
It was the middle of winter and heavy rain fell, driven by a
raw north-easterly wind. But by early afternoon, as the cortege
was starting to assemble at Cragside, the rain eased off a little
and there was a good turn-out of local people. When the
majority of mourners had assembled outside the house, a farm
cart covered with a rich purple cloth and drawn by two farm-
horses was driven up and upon this the coffin and the wreaths
were placed. Another farm cart bore the rest of the wreaths.
Shortly after one o'clock the melancholy procession set off,
drawing the body of Lord Armstrong through the extensive
grounds, now silent, wet and cold, that he had created. The
journey lasted an hour; the service but a few minutes. In
keeping with the style of the man it was simple and un-
affected. He might have become one of England's greatest
industrialists, yet he was delighted to go skating with small
boys. He might have had honorary degrees almost piled on him
and the presidency of this learned body or that professional
institution conferred upon him but he was never happier than
when he was alone in his laboratory. Now that tremendous
energy was stilled. The life of outstanding achievement was
over. He was buried in Rothbury churchyard next to his wife,
who had died seven years before him.

# CHAPTER NINE

## CONCLUSION

'THERE is something that appals the imagination in the cool application of a clear and temperate mind like Lord Armstrong's to the science of destruction.' The *Newcastle Daily Chronicle's* obituary words stated succinctly the moral dilemma facing Armstrong and his colleagues. Over the next thirty years or so the argument was to be widened and developed as the pacificists urged the prohibition of private arms manufacture. In pursuing their case, they accused Armstrong and his successors of all sort of crimes from bribery to double-dealing, from the deliberate creation of war scares to the planned obsolescence of ordnance. The words spoken by Undershaft in Bernard Shaw's play, *Major Barbara*, became the motto of all they suspected: 'To give arms to all men who offer an honest price for them without respect of persons or principles.' The arms manufacturer was a man without honour or conscience.

Were the arguments and the accusations fair? A Royal Commission that was set up by the Government thought not. After a detailed investigation, it found no evidence of the bribery that was alleged to be so frequent, of the deliberate creation of war scares, of the playing off of one country against another and of all the other malevolent tactics that critics claimed were part of the everyday life of the private arms manufacturer. On the contrary, the Royal Commission found that there were very good arguments for allowing the private industry to continue. The most important was that unless there were private manufacturers in peace time, essential capacity for war purposes would be lacking or not quickly available. The First World War itself provided excellent evidence to support this argument. The private manufacturers played then a vital role. The War also provided, as it were, a climax to Armstrong's work—even though he had been dead for fourteen years.

In the early years of the War, before the National Factories were established, there were three main sources of supply for ordnance: the Government works at Woolwich; Vickers, and Armstrong Whitworth. It was on these three concerns, therefore, that the massive weight of ordnance demands fell. Not only were the demands themselves incredibly large but they had to be met in the face of certain severe problems. Armstrong, Whitworth, for example, had not carried out any work on land service armaments for many years. The pre-war requirements of the Regular Army had been fully met by Woolwich so that Armstrong Whitworth and Vickers had concentrated on naval work. Consequently, there were no important resources of plant or machinery immediately available for the production of artillery for the Army. Secondly, the private manufacturers were looked upon as 'maids of all work', of whom any demands could be made. In the early years of the war, there were times when Armstrong, Whitworth was producing simultaneously more than 70 different types of shell and a wide range of guns. Such a range called for a constant readjustment of machinery and an extra need for careful supervision. A bare statement of the output figures hardly brings out the organizational problems involved.

Yet the figures themselves are impressive and hold a special magic. During those four years, Armstrong Whitworth produced the enormous total of 13,000 guns, most of them complete with carriages, and 100 of the earliest types of tanks. It also produced an incredible quantity of shell. At the outbreak of war, the Elswick capacity for projectiles was between 35 and 40 tons a week, for cartridge cases about 1,000 items a week and for fuses about 500 a week. Within a few months shell output went up to 8,000 a week and continued to increase throughout the war. The grand total in the four years exceeded 14,500,000. About 18,500,000 fuses were produced and 21,000,000 cartridge cases.

The warship output was a staggering story in itself. Altogether, 47 warships were built, including battleships and cruisers. In addition, 62 warships were fitted with newer and more powerful armaments and 240 merchant ships were so fitted. The Walker yard also produced 22 merchant ships during this period. Heavy actions at sea, for example at Heligoland Bight, Dogger Bank and Jutland, resulted in an urgent demand for extensive repairs and this side of the firm's work became as important as new ship production. Over 130 ships a year were repaired and refitted.

Even this is not the end. For the firm was one of the pioneers in aviation. By the time the war began, Armstrong Whitworth had carried out a good deal of experimental work and had completed six aeroplanes. This new capacity was now to be tapped increasingly. In 1914, the firm built eight machines. By 1918 the number was up to 429 and altogether during the war well over 1,000 aeroplanes were produced. This figure does not include the three airships R.23, R.29, R.33. The R.29, with a one and a half million cubic feet capacity, was particularly successful and sunk a number of German submarines in the North Sea.

Where would the country have been without this enormous contribution to its defence? Can it really be argued that it was the supply of weapons of increasing power during the previous half-century that in itself caused the War? Or would it be more accurate to say that the development of newer and bigger weapons coincided with growing nationalistic and imperialist ambitions in many countries throughout the world? If one takes the latter view then clearly the private arms manufacturer was one of two means of gaining supplies. The Government could have substituted work by its own departments. The private industry was used because it was the better of the two. It was as simple as that. If, however, one takes the view that the arms manufacturer was the demon who inspired the First World War and other conflicts, then clearly he must have been an enormously, indeed impossibly powerful figure—able not only to produce weapons but to sway the defence and foreign policies of countries throughout the world. Stated like that, the argument is absurd but it puts into relief the weakness of the critics' case. It might still be argued that the arms manufacurer cannot be absolved from his personal responsibility. Armstrong did not see it like that. He felt that by improving the design and performance of armaments, he was reducing the barbarity of war. What is more, weapons were not something new. They had been in existence for thousands

of years. It was man himself, not the arms manufacturer, who
was to blame. Take away modern weapons and human beings
would revert to wooden clubs with which to maim and kill one
another. In short, the pacifist case was too simple and super-
ficial. It failed to look to the deep-seated psychological explanations for wars and threats of wars.

Today, we can perhaps see Armstrong in a clearer and more
reasonable light than the generation that immediately followed
him. They were appalled by the horror of the First World
War when battles ceased to be romantic affairs in far-off
lands. Now, after countless other conflicts, we can recognize
that only changes in man himself will eliminate wars and the
need for the arms manufacturer.

For the rest of Armstrong's work, one can today feel nothing
but admiration, particularly for his ability to combine scientific
research of the first importance with a business sense of obvious
shrewdness. To have carried out complicated programmes into
electrical and mechanical research, to have applied his
researches by building cranes and guns and to have combined
all this with the business ability which nurtured a factory with
20,000 employees—this was a remarkable combination of
characteristics. Without doubt, they earn him a place among
that small group of entrepreneurs who literally created
industrial Britain.

# CHAPTER NOTES

**INTRODUCTION**
1. Johnson, R. W. 'The Making of the Tyne', p. 278.

**CHAPTER ONE**
1. Dolmon, F. 'The Ludgate Monthly', Oct. 1900, p. 575.
2. Ibid.
3. Richardson, J. W. 'Memoirs', p. 32.
4. Newcastle Town Council Minutes, 9th Nov. 1846, p. 16-17.

**CHAPTER TWO**
1. Bernal, J. D. 'Science in History, Vol. 2, p. 544.
2. Middlebrook, S. 'Newcastle Upon Tyne, its Growth and Achievement', p. 185.
3. Bernal, J. D. Ibid, p. 547.
4. Rendel, Lord, The Personal Papers Of, p. 268.
5. Dolman, F. Ibid, p. 574.
6. The Northern Counties Magazine, Oct. 1900, p. 7.
7. Monthly Chronicle of North Country Lore & Legend, Jan. 1889, p. 3.

**CHAPTER THREE**
1. Trevelyan, G. M. 'A Shortened History of England', p. 487.
2. Pemberton, W. B. 'Battles of the Crimean War', p. 162.
3. Rendel, Lord. Ibid, p. 269-270.
4. Armstrong, W. G. 'Industrial Resources, Tyne, Wear and Tees', p. 269.
5. Rendel, Lord. Ibid, p. 271.
6. Cochrane, A. 'The Early History of Elswick', p. 76.
7. 152 H. C. Deb, 3s., 1859, col. 1319.
8. S. C. on Ordnance H. of C. 448 in P.P. Vol. VI of 1862 W. 2309.
9. The Northern Counties Magazine, Oct. 1900, p. 14.
10. The Newcastle Journal, 14th May 1859, p. 7.
11. Address to the Institute of Mechanical Engineers, p. 189.
12. Newcastle Journal, 14th May 1859, p. 7.
13. Rendel, Lord. Ibid, p. 272.

CHAPTER FOUR

1. Hay, R. J. Letter to Armstrong, quoted in Armstrong's letter to The Times, 25th Nov. 1861.

2. Halsted, Capt. Letter to The Times, quoted in Armstrong's letter to The Times, 25th Nov. 1861, p. 15.

3. Armstrong, W. G. Letter to The Times, 25th Nov. 1861.

4. Address to Institute of Mechanical Engineers, p. 193.

5. Rendel, Lord. Ibid, p. 274.

6. The Times, leading article, 9th Oct. 1861.

7. Tennent, Sir Emerson, 'The Story of the Guns', p. 149.

8. Ordnance Select Committee Report, 1861, App. 551.

9. Ibid, Appendix, p. 305.

10. Rendel, Lord. Ibid, p. 275-276.

11. Armstrong, W. G. 'Industrial Resources of Tyne, Wear and Tees', p. 15.

CHAPTER FIVE

1. Institution of Civil Engineers, Minutes at mtg., 15th May 1867.

2. Rendel, Lord. Ibid, p. 280-281.

3. The Gatling Gun Papers, Newcastle City Archives.

CHAPTER SIX

1. Middlebrook, S. Ibid. p. 185.

2. Armstrong, W. G. Ibid, p. 20.

3. Armstrong, W. G. 'A Trip to Egypt', Newcastle 1874.

4. Worsnop, John. Reminiscences in Newcastle Daily Journal, 28th Dec. 1900, p. 5.

CHAPTER SEVEN

1. Manning, Frederick, 'The Life of Sir William White', p. 42.

2. Manning, Frederick. Ibid, p. 178.

3. Richardson, W. 'A History of the Parish of Wallsend', p. 465.

4. Richardson, W. Ibid, p. 360.

5. Modern Naval Artillery, Anon., London 1887, p. 3.

6. The Jubilee Chronicle, Newcastle 1887, p. 23.

7. R. W. Johnson, 'The Making of the Tyne', Newcastle 1895.

8. Newcastle Daily Chronicle, 18th Nov. 1882, p. 3.

9. Northern Counties Magazine, Nov. 1900, p. 76.

CHAPTER EIGHT

1. Newcastle Daily Leader, 14th June 1886, p. 4.

2. Ibid, 7th July 1886, p. 4.

3. Ibid, 21st June 1887, p. 4.

# SOURCES

Armstrong, W. G. 'Industrial Resources of Tyne, Wear and Tees'. Transactions of British Association meeting, Newcastle, 1863.
Armstrong, Sir W. G. 'Addresses by' (Newcastle City Library).
Armstrong, Sir W. G. 'A Visit to Egypt in 1872'. Four lectures to the Literary and Philosophical Society.

Bean, David. 'Armstrong's Men', Newcastle 1967.
Berdrow, Wilhelm. 'Letters of Alfred Krupp 1826-1887' edited by, transl. E. W. Dickens, London, 1930.
Bruce, 'Handbook to Newcastle on Tyne', Newcastle, 1863.
Bernal, J. D. 'Science in History', Vol. 2, London 1954.

Cochrane, Alfred. 'The Early History of Elswick', Newcastle, 1909.
Collection of Items Relating to Lord Armstrong. Local History Section, Newcastle City Library.
Clark, J. F. 'Industrial Relations in the North East, 1850-1914', M. A. Thesis, Newcastle University, 1966.
Council of Civil Engineers, 'Sir W. G. Armstrong and Company and Mr. J. Scott Russell', Minutes of meetings relating to charge against Mr. Scott Russell of indebtedness, fraud, embezzlement or larceny. Newcastle City Library.

Emerson-Tennent, Sir J. 'The Story of the Guns', London 1864.
'Elswick, 1847-1947', Vickers Brochure, Newcastle 1948.

Fordyce, Local Records. Nc. 1867. Literary and Philosophical Society.

Hume, George. 'The History of the Newcastle Infirmary' Nc. 1906, Lit. & Phil.

Johnson, R. W. 'The Making of the Tyne', Nc. 1895.

Lewis, Michael. 'The History of the British Navy', London, 1957.
Lawson, 'Tyneside Celebrities', Newcastle.

Manchester, William. 'The Arms of Krupp'. London, 1969.

Middlebrook, S. 'Newcastle, Its Growth & Achievements'. Newcastle, 1950.

Manning, Frederick. 'The Life of Sir Wm. White', London, 1923.

Monthly Record of Eminent Men, Newcastle, August 1891.

Northern Counties Magazine, Vol. 1. Two articles on Elswick, Oct. and Nov. 1900.

Noble, Sir Andrew. 'Artillery & Explosives'.

Noble, Mark. 'Men of the North', Newcastle City Library.

Newcastle Courant. Various dates, 1847.

N.E. Coast Exhibition, 1882. Brochure, Newcastle City Library.

Plummer, 'Newcastle its Trade and Manufactures', Newcastle, 1874.

Pemberton, W. G. 'Battles of the Crimean War, London, 1962.

Rendel, Lord. The Personal Papers Of. London, 1931.

Richardson, J. W. Memoirs. Glasgow, 1911.

Scott, J. D. 'Vickers—A History', London, 1962.

Spence Watson, R. W. 'The History of the Lit. & Phil. Society', Newcastle, 1901.

Swan, Sir Joseph Wilson, Nc. 1929.

Trevelyan, G. M. 'A Shortened History of England', London 1959.

Various Writers. 'Fortunes Made In Business', London, 1887.

Welford Richard, 'Men of Mark 'Twixt Tyne & Tees', Vol. 1.

# Index

## Also published by Sandhill Press

### AS THEY WERE
compiled by R. Thompson Dix
*A nostalgic glimpse of life from old photographs of North Shields, Tynemouth, Cullercoats, Whitley Bay & Wallsend.*

### A BASINFUL O' GEORDIE
by Dorfy
*A selection of humorous Tyneside readings in dialect.*

### THE BODY IN THE BANK : Famous Northern murders
Retold by Sandhill Press
*A fascinating collection of murders, trials and subsequent harsh punishments which took place in our northern towns and the surrounding countryside.*

### THE BORDER REIVERS
by Godfrey Watson
*A must for the many people called Armstrong, Scott, Charlton, Robson, Bell... in whose veins runs the blood of the 'Reivers'.*

### CUSTOMS & TRADITIONS OF NORTHUMBRIA
Retold by Sandhill Press
*Ceremonies, seasons and times of the year, leisure & work activities are set against an historical background of events in the area..*

### GHOSTS & LEGENDS OF NORTHUMBRIA
Retold by Sandhill Press
*A collection of famous tales of ghosts, hauntings and strange happenings that form part of the folklore of Northumbria.*

### THE LAST YEARS OF A FRONTIER
by D.L.W. Tough
*A history of the Borders during the turbulent times of Elizabeth I.*

### MAD DOGS & CYCLISTS
by Chris Rooney
*Rich lyrical prose and humorous anecdote are combined to relate the joys of cycling in Northumbria.*

**MEDIEVAL CASTLES, TOWERS, PELES & BASTLES OF
NORTHUMBERLAND**
by T.H. Rowland

**NORTHUMBRIA IN PICTURES**
compiled by Beryl Sanderson
*A new revised edition of our successful colour souvenir guide-
superb photographs and accompanying text.*

**NORTHUMBRIAN COASTLINE**
by Ian Smith
*A walker's guide to the area from Berwick upon Tweed to North
Shields, printed in the author's own handwriting and including his
many line drawings and maps.*

**NORTHUMBRIAN PUB : an architectural history**
by Lynn F. Pearson
*A social and architectural history of our northern pubs.*

**ROGUES & REIVERS OF THE NORTH COUNTRY**
Retold by Sandhill Press
*Tales of highwaymen, smugglers, bodysnatchers and
the notorious Border Reivers.*

**UPPER COQUETDALE**
by David Dippie Dixon
*Northumberland : its history, traditions, folklore and scenery.
Originally published in 1903 - a special limited numbered edition.*

**VICTORIAN & EDWARDIAN NORTHUMBRIA
FROM OLD PHOTOGRAPHS**
by J.W. Thompson & D. Bond.

**WARKWORTH**
by Ian Smith
*A charming guide to this unique Northumbrian village.*

**YORKSHIRE COASTLINE**
by Ian Smith
*A second guide covering the coast from the Tees to Bridlington.*